The Multiple's Guide To Harmonized Family Living

A Healthy Alternative (Or Prelude) To Integration

By Tammy Colleen Whitman
&
Susan C. Shore, Ph.D.

Artistic Endeavors Publishing

Marina Del Rey, California

The Multiple's Guide To Harmonized Family Living

A Healthy Alternative (Or Prelude) To Integration

By Tammy Colleen Whitman
&
Susan C. Shore, Ph.D.

Published by:

Artistic Endeavors Publishing
P.O. Box 10224-P
Marina Del Rey, CA 90292 USA

First Printing, 1994
Printed in the United States of America

Publisher's Cataloging in Publication Data
Whitman, Tammy Colleen
The Multiple's Guide To Harmonized Family Living: A Healthy Alternative (or Prelude) to Integration / by Tammy Colleen Whitman and Susan C. Shore
1st Edition.

p. cm

Includes bibliographical references

Includes index.

616.85 1994 94-70635

ISBN 1-884390-03-X $16.95 Soft cover

Library of Congress Catalog Card Number: 94-70635

Table of Contents

Warning - Disclaimer

Because examples of situations and behaviors are described to clarify our information, it is possible that certain survivors going through very difficult and unstable times might do well to read this with their therapist or with a supportive friend.

In addition, because incest and childhood sexual abuse cuts across all races, religions, and genders, it is not possible to use terms that will fit in with everyone's orientation regarding their system, religions, the Spirit, or Higher Power, God, etc. We have tried to remain neutral in addressing the general Multiple Personality audience, and want you to know we respect and hope to augment whatever sources of healing you have aligned yourself with in your recovery.

This book is designed to provide information on harmonization, and to educate and entertain the reader. It is sold with the understanding that it is not intended to be a substitute for therapy and if expert assistance is needed, we strongly suggest you seek the advice of a competent professional.

It is not the purpose of this book to provide all available information on the subject of Multiple Personality Disorder, but, simply, to add to the existing body of knowledge and to compliment and augment the healing process. Further, it is not intended to be a cure all. All material within these pages are strictly suggestions that worked for us, and others, and may not be appropriate for your recovery track.

The authors and Artistic Endeavors Publishing shall not be held liable, nor responsible, to any person for any psychological or physical distress or damages caused directly or indirectly (alleged or actual), by the information or contents of this book.

If you do not wish to be bound by the above, you may return this book in its original condition within 15 days of purchase, to the place of purchase, for a full refund.

Acknowledgments

We wish to acknowledge our friends who helped get our newsletter M.U.L.T.I.P.L.E. launched over a year ago, and who's support and encouragement of our work with non-integrated Multiples motivated us to write this book. They are Karen K., of *S.O.F.I.E.*, Lin and Seth Cawthra, of *The MAZE* and *S.H.A.R.E.*, Jo Finn, former editor of *Speaking Out*, Beth Hafling, of *B.E.A.M.*, as well as the many people, M.P.D.'s and therapists, who have taken time out of their lives to write in with questions and praise for our work. You are all very dear to us!

My inner family, and myself, extend a very special thanks to Margie Cunningham who's generous gift allowed us to print this book. Further, we wish to thank our co-author and most dearest friend and extended family member, Susan. We are blessed to have you in our lives for there is no finer role model or mentor in the world. We love you!

- Tammy & Family

I, personally, want to thank my colleagues who have pioneered research and understanding in human potential and are authors, teachers, and therapists themselves. First are Adam Crabtree and Dr. Stanley Krippner, kindred souls in paranormal phenomena, who endorsed my research and encouraged me to write about what I am learning from survivors. Secondly, I'd like to extend a special thanks to Dr. Winafred Lucas, Diplomate ABPP, who has been a faithful mentor and supportive friend for many years.

- Susan Shore, Ph.D.

Cover and chapter artwork produced by our in-house artist,
Susan Shore, Ph.D.

Book design and layout by Michael.
Poetry and verse, a collective effort.

Dedication

This book is dedicated to all childhood sexual abuse survivors suffering and/or prospering with Multiple Personality Disorder, who, at best, have been long misunderstood and the subject of much suspicion by the medical community and society in general. It is also written to honor the numerous victims who died before they found the help, validation, and direction they so desperately needed and deserved.

It is our hope that treating professionals will one day come to understand our pain, and view multiplicity as the creative response to intolerable circumstances and suffering that it is, and not, necessarily, as a disease or disorder from which we need curing. We pray they will be encouraged by our results, and courageous enough to adapt their therapeutic methods to include ours and bring about favorable, lasting change and self-empowerment in those still hurting and dysfunctional.

Preface

Though we are rapidly learning, since the early 80's, about the large incidence and extensive ramifications of childhood and ritual abuse, there is still a lack of comprehensive understanding about the inner workings of dissociative minds. The emerging pathology of Multiple Personality Disorder (recently changed to Dissociative Identity Disorder), particularly, holds many challenges for treating professionals who have unanswered questions as to the nature and formation of this condition. Paramount in effectively dismantling this, would be to understand how the mind recreates or reorganizes its inner properties, were that the necessary goal. We, at M.U.L.T.I.P.L.E., have a different perspective on this issue.

Despite professional assumptions, I have learned from survivors who have undergone "successful" treatment that integration does not cure the effects of childhood abuse at all. The residual pains from terrifying memories resulting in unhealthy patterns of relating to others, and the self-inflicted violence, all remain part of a life no longer a Multiple Personality nor worth living. Consequently, survivors are coming out of treatment feeling betrayed, disillusioned, and compromised in their choice of their inner "family's" existence, by a therapist with an agenda.

It may surprise professionals, but I have reason to believe there are a lot more individuals with multiple minds *not* seeking treatment for their mental condition than those who are, as is evidenced by the dozens of letters of encouragement I receive each month, and read in other survivor publications, from Multiples.

Most of the survivors I have seen or read about, wish healing from the pain and traumatic experiences they relive daily from the memories of severely abusive childhoods, and not, necessarily, from their multiplicity. Eliminating multiplicity not only does not heal the abuse, but can overwhelm a survivor with an enormous amount of traumatic material because it strips them of their defenses. "A shift of mind does not cure or erase a horrible childhood, or the emotional aftermath of destructive behavior patterns any more than medications do.... Furthermore, recovery has been reported to be a life long process for those individuals who are integrated, as for those who are not." (Shore, 1993. "A Challenge to Professionals")

Unfortunately, I have come to understand that many Multiples who need help and understanding avoid therapists because they read our literature, treatment goals, and all the books about M.P.D. cases who are "cured" because they have integrated. This need not be the only happy ending. They are just the ones professionals and integrated subjects get publicized the most as examples of successful treatment.

Consequently, we started M.U.L.T.I.P.L.E. so that survivors would have support available from a qualified comprehending professional as the publisher, and an experienced, well-adjusted, and non-integrated harmonized Multiple as the editor if they choose not to integrate (and it's fine if they seek integration), to educate them in alternatives, provide a forum for self-expression, and a place to network for support. In addition, we have made available a number of self-directed healing tapes to augment the survivor's own recovery process that can be used alone or with their therapist, as well as a crisis management and stabilization telephone consulting service for treating professionals.

It is important to note here, that co-conscious cooperation

among Alter persons is a viable step toward integration, if that is the client's choice. Consequently, all of our methods or suggestions for self-directed healing would enhance any therapeutic track for persons with dissociative conditions, and will not conflict with integrative goals. I have noticed some M.P. clients on harmonization tracks have, subsequently, decided to strive for integration and felt that to be a natural progression from where they were. This supports my observation that each client is capable of recognizing their own needs, and timing for fulfilling those needs, without any prodding from me.

I remind professionals that part of the therapeutic process for the client is to achieve autonomy in their own healing and experiment in learning what works best for them. This process of self-discovery is interfered with every time a well-meaning therapist imposes a prescribed agenda or program on a client. In essence, they are telling them "I know what's best for you, and you need to listen to me to know what is right and do what I tell you." This only fosters co-dependency. I am not trying to imply we shouldn't make suggestions, or offer techniques in healing, or coping methods for resolving distress. I am simply saying that allowing options and encouraging exploration of alternatives for a survivor stripped of all their power and sense of self, would be beneficial in slowly developing confidence in themselves and their decision making abilities.

The focus for Multiples in recovery is rebuilding authenticity of themselves, their feelings, and a sense of worth out of the wreckage of a devastated childhood. Telling them what they have to be in your professional view (i.e., integrated) is not going to promote or accomplish self-empowerment one bit, and raises valid concerns among those living with this condition.

Clients will feel unresolved when they discover that integration did not fix how they feel about themselves, how they interact with others, nor wipe out the memories of callous betrayals by their loved ones. Furthermore, achieving integration does not make the world an easier place to live in, or lighten up the social and economic demands. In fact, some integrated clients, who decided to revert into multiplicity for safety, viewed giving up life saving coping mechanisms with such challenges ahead as a formula for failure.

As far as professionals believing that integration is in the best interest of the client in the long run, I have mixed feelings. Didn't we once believe that all homosexuals were disordered, and that they would be much better off if they could shed their attraction to the same sex? In retrospect, was that opinion for us or them? I'm sure homophobics would be happier. More appropriately to ask, would they be a better person? Though the world might be a calmer place if we were all the same, as is indicated in our current social unrest, I think tolerating diversity with support and compassion is a necessary component in our social and spiritual evolution.

Has our professional history repeated itself in assuming something is sick or undesirable because it is different? Minds within minds are different, but they can be functional, knowledgeable, and we can learn from them if we allow them their uniqueness.

I have seen this evidenced in recovering Multiples who have learned to accept their truths, released their pain, and came out valuing themselves as unique, talented, resourceful beings. I have observed cooperative inner "families" that pitch in for one another when one is down and carry on with responsibility and sensitivity in a way that is admirable. Furthermore, I have watched them establish healthy, caring, committed interpersonal relationships within, and with others outside who could appreciate them in their diversity.

In closing, I have one final question. Have we, as a profession, gone overboard by claiming to know not only what is wrong with someone, but ascribing for them what will make them happy?

- Dr. Susan Shore, Publisher

Bark Bark!!
Stay Out

Chapter One

Learning About Your System and Its Residents

Introduction

Multiplicity is a complex mind configuration that is, generally, the result of extreme repeated trauma (usually sexual) experienced at an early age when physical escape, and/or, avoidance was impossible. Though a lot has recently been written about the condition and its effects on the lives of those who have it, there is still too little understanding about the nature and capabilities of this unique response to childhood abuse. Sadly, most of the available literature, written primarily by professionals considered "experts" in the field of M.P.D., claim complete integration of the various "parts" to be the only healthy outcome of treatment for multiplicity.

We find this disturbing, as we, like many other Multiples, do not experience ourselves as disordered in the usual sense of the word, nor as "parts". Multiplicity, we came to realize after many unfulfilling attempts at fusion and integration, was not the cause of our problems, and thus, was not what needed "curing". Similarly, it was not the reason for our recurrent failures at getting well. The catalysts that perpetuated our dysfunction and repeated retreats into chaos, we found, were the scores of unresolved memories of trauma and abuse held in our individual psyches, that were overflowing into our behavior when we were distressed. By trying to eliminate the multiplicity we lost sight of our goal, which was, ultimately, to heal from our pasts and become well-adjusted, functional members of society. When we finally gave up trying to fit into psychology's narrow definition of "normal" and accepted ourselves as merely atypical, not abnormal, we were able to make real progress in our recovery. Subsequently, we combined our strengths and talents to form the loving family we always wished we had as children, and we continue to grow closer and more caring toward each other with each passing day.

It took a great deal of struggling, soul searching, adjusting of attitudes, and shedding of tears before we were able to readjust our roles and establish a cohesive bond between us. However, in choosing harmonization (a mutually pleasing arrangement between Alters) over the therapeutic dictum of forced integration, we became strong and confident in our abilities to manage our own lives in a productive, loving manner. That is why we have written this book, to present Multiples questioning the necessity of integration, a healthy alternative course of treatment should they wish to try it. We do not imply that your lives will be perfect, or that you will not encounter difficulties along the way. We simply appreciate that many Multiples (in treatment and not in treatment) may have a desire to make their own informed decisions regarding the course of treatment they wish to pursue in their recovery. Our choice in harmonization has allowed us to become autonomous from the mental health system, find peace within ourselves, and to establish a group sense of self-empowerment. Furthermore, it has established a strong foundation of cooperation should we, collectively, decide to work toward integration in the future.

Getting to Know Your Inner Persons

Have you heard the saying "It takes all kinds to make a world?" Well, similarly, it takes all kinds of personality types to make up a Multiple's system. Getting to know all the players of your inner team completely enough to function as a well-adjusted family, requires a great deal of hard work and personal sacrifice on everyone's part. After all, like the links that make up an iron chain, a family, be it your's or mine, "is only as strong is it's weakest member."

You may say, self-assuredly, "but we're already a family, and a pretty good one at that!" However, simply saying or believing you are a family, is not the same as *being* a well-adjusted, loving, functional family. Though it is not my intention to tear down your system, I would ask, "have you gotten to know each and every one of the persons within your system extensively (adults, guardians, children, elders, etc.)?" For instance, do you know their full names, their ethnic background, or who they patterned themselves after? Do you know such things as their basic operating principles, what things upset them, or make them happy? Do you know the kind of food they like, the clothes they prefer to wear, the hair styles they favor, or their favorite colors? Or, how about their sexual orientation, range of moods, or their feelings about being an Alter? Furthermore, do you know why they were created, what deep, dark secrets they harbor, or where they stand on important issues?

Just as a lot of time and personal investment goes into making and keeping friends, so it goes with learning the most intimate details of each person acting within your system. To be uninformed about key aspects of any Alter's characteristics is leaving the "budding family" open to potential ruin. Learning right off the bat where the "hot spots" are in a relationship, helps not only to develop good instincts and respect for one another, but it also allows each party to explore the "fabric" they are weaving for irregularities that could spoil the best laid plans.

For instance, if you find out that "Thomas" is a wonderful negotiator but despises policemen, it would be in the best interest of the family unit not to allow him into the body after you have just been stopped for speeding. Regardless of the "silver tongued devil's" abilities, his tendency toward violence where law officers are concerned could land you, and your inner family, in more trouble than you bargained for.

A good example of this would be a Multiple who suddenly finds the body incarcerated because an uncooperative Alter broke the law and was caught. The unruly or inconsiderate Alter might not care that he has been imprisoned, however, the rest of your inner family certainly will (who are incarcerated as well). In addition, your future economic security (unable to secure employment opportunities because of a prison record) may be seriously jeopardized.

Furthermore, operating with only part of an Alter person's cooperation may be detrimental to the whole as well. I have observed that some Alters who, initially, do not want to participate may promise to keep to themselves and not effect the daily running of the family. However, there will be times when personal conflicts of their needs and yours will arise, and, if not anticipated well in advance, can cause strife between members. For example, a promise made to a child Alter to go out to lunch, only to have it broken by "Alex" who took control of the body so he could go to the library, will upset the child. The child Alter might not be able to understand anything except that her promised outing was spoiled, and thus becomes angry at "Alex", triggering a defensive reaction. Since "Alex" never invested himself fully in cooperating for the benefit of the whole, he defends himself by calling the angry child names and a war breaks out between camps. Like the saying goes "To be forewarned is to be forearmed." It would be prudent to get an agreement with the child beforehand, that if something should come up which interferes with the plans for your outing, that you will go at another time and mark the alternative date on your calendar. Should that occur, it would be wise to post the new date where everyone can see it to avoid another disappointment.

So, start right now to get to know the actors within your scripts (sort of speak). "Take the bull by the horns" and introduce yourself to someone inside who you are not thoroughly acquainted with. Maybe someone at the back of the room, or, depending on the set up of your communal structure, the other side of "town". If this is scary for you, children are the easiest to approach and are more likely to respond favorably to friendly contact. Start with them and work your way around to the others. Of course, use caution in how you go about it. No one likes to be steam rolled, or intimidated. That is how their abusers treated them.

Be careful of each Alter's property and don't snoop or handle their personal possessions. They would like to feel, as you would, that their space will be respected if they graciously allow someone into it. Remember, however, that getting to know your inner persons is not a one time process, or something that will happen overnight. Set aside a specific amount of time each day, or week, to show interest in your Alters by meeting for conversation, if they are amenable, take the children Alters to the park or zoo, or, if nothing else, just to hang out together.

You may be surprised to find out, through casual conversation, how much you have in common with your inner persons. Furthermore, you may discover that the Alter you thought had no purpose, or was merely created to be the "brute" during physical altercations, is actually highly intelligent with some pretty amazing ideas for a business, or, perhaps, he possesses skills you believed were lacking from your collective talent bank.

When you have successfully begun to relate with this person, introduce yourself to another, and another, until you know all of those who are agreeable to a relationship among you. Don't be overly concerned, however, if some persons do not wish to become friends with you right away. Keep in mind, that Alters are seldom, if ever, created out of loving, healthy interactions, so it may take some time for them to learn to trust you, and others, before they allow themselves to be open.

Another important thing to remember while building your allies, is that some Alters have specific psychological agendas. There will be some who are always pleasant and non-threatening and a major help in organizing support for your mission, while others may be frightened beyond participation, delusional, or vindictive and unruly. Reaching them will take more time, effort, patience, and, perhaps, professional assistance. Steer clear of those who are not ready to join forces, and just observe their reactions, over time, to the changes taking place around them. Alters who were created to protect, defend, or handle rage, for instance, may surreptitiously try to undermine your plan if they perceive your efforts as "boat rocking" by uprooting their role and influence, or attempts to upset the "status quo".

Certain persons who where created to be arbitrators, guardians, bosses, gatekeepers, etc., or even the core person (if you know who that is), may be able to assist you in approaching these more difficult members sometime down the road, or may be willing to serve as a mediator. Such authority figures, generally, have detailed knowledge of each Alter person's weaknesses, strengths, issues, and fears. In addition, they may be more aware of what a person inwardly wishes for or needs. Don't be afraid to ask for their assistance, and then let them guide you when the time is right.

Subsequently, as time passes and more Alters work on themselves, the non-participants will begin to envy the positive changes, the evolving love that is demonstrated for one another, and the family outings you will all come to enjoy. They may start out feeling resentful why this camaraderie was not there for them when they needed it. However, as they see the new relationships strengthen and endure over time, their own longing to have a better life for themselves will grow stronger as they are able to trust this new found stability and experience hope. If the time is right, they may ask to join in, if not, they may need more time just to observe. Whatever you do, don't push! Some of us process pain, and even positive change, at different rates. They will come around in their own time.

You will start experiencing, as you become friends with some of your Alters, that you miss their company when they are not around. You will wish to spend increasing amounts of time together working on projects, and helping the children and the dysfunctional Alters to express themselves through artwork, role play exercises, and casual conversation. The camaraderie between you will be a wonderful feeling, especially, because you all share a common bond and endured a tragic history. This is your family now. Take pride in them, and yourself, and allow *no one* to trespass on your special time together. Let down your defenses at these times and do whatever you heart is leading you to do. Get down on the floor and pretend you are a horse if that's what you want to do, color with the kids, play Jacks, or just lay on your backs drinking in the warm rays of the sun. It's up to you! It's your community and family, and no one can dictate to you what is acceptable and what is not.

Exploring Your Inner Structure

Another important aspect of your system to become acquainted with, is the physical structure and characteristics of your inner world. These inner worlds have proven to be constructed uniquely by each Multiple, and learning about yours will require some amount of investigation. Some Multiples claim to have one room where all the persons reside, while others, such as ours, have more elaborate designs resembling whole towns or a village. Sometimes there are multilevel systems with undergrounds and tiers, while others resemble a galaxy of planets and stars. Similarly, some have only a curtain separating the inside from the body. We, on the other hand, have a two-way window through which I can monitor what's happening inside, while in the body, and the inner persons, should they wish, can merely glance through as they walk by to see what's happening on the outside.

When I first began to relate to my inner persons, I noticed that the inner surroundings were very dark, cold, and relatively quiet. In fact, in many ways, the disquieting stillness resembled the eeriness of a morgue. However, over time, as I worked with my inner persons to process their trauma and fear, the inside began to brighten slowly, as if someone were controlling the light level with a dimmer switch. When this happened, I was able to see that we had constructed a clearly delineated communal habitat that had numerous rooms and cottages, a stream, green grass, a brick walkway, mountain ranges, and even a push-go-round for the children to play on.

In addition, each Alter had personal items or paraphernalia of their own. Grizzly, for example, had erected a basketball hoop, where he shot baskets when he was bored, Michael had a lawn mower which he used to drown out the noise of his troubling thoughts, Jessie had horses and little animals to entertain her, and Sister Mary designed her room with stained glass windows and an alter to kneel at while she prayed. One Alter even had a fully stocked library of his favorite books and a big leather chair in which to sit and read.

Upon further investigation, which took many months, we found ground level trap doors scattered around the compound that led to an underground system of tunnels, caverns, and sleep chambers, watched over by guardian Alters. We're not sure who built the tunnels and caverns, but we suspect they house systematically or cult abused Alters, who are destructive and stuck in their programming from traumatic experiences at a very early time in our lives. The actual events, at this point, are still unknown to us, though we have dreams that support this theory.

Subsequently, as we continued to investigate our inner town, we realized these trap doors were placed strategically around the property, which negative Alters and entities used to telepathically attack Jessie and Michael when they were psychotic. By boarding up these secret entrance ways, we, virtually, stopped all their harassment, and Jessie's and Michael's episodes diminished entirely. Furthermore, closing off these entrances provided safety and a sense of well-being among the frightened children Alters who had been afraid to venture very far outside their own spaces.

We strongly recommend you get to know your system thoroughly, explore all the nooks and crannies (though not alone), and find out what is good and what is not within your system. As you investigate, you will discover that a lot happens on the inside that you were not aware of, which causes your Alters added distress and worry. Take any action toward making their world safer that you deem appropriate. Furthermore, we noticed that the more negativity we released while becoming more cooperative and caring, the brighter and more pleasant our inner structure became. In essence, because we all share in the mind's energy field, our own turmoil and distress was giving off a lot of darkness, like pollution, into our environment. As we each became more loving, we radiated more positive energy, changing the quality of our inner atmosphere. Wouldn't you prefer to come out of the dark and live in a warmer, brighter, calmer, and loving atmosphere? You will, once your collective starts working together on improving yourselves.

Establishing and Respecting Boundaries

As I have already mentioned, it is crucial to respect the boundaries established by Alters or you may risk personal injury or turn someone against you. As each person has had different experiences in their lifetime, each, also, has their own individual ways of relating to their environment. "The Withdrawn One", for example, may be very depressed and appreciate her privacy. Though she is unlikely to physically harm anyone if it is not in her nature, she may become more withdrawn and mistrusting of you. It would be considerate and respectful, in this case, not to invade her space without permission. The quickest way to grow to dislike someone is to be continuously interrupted by them when you prefer to be alone. I cannot stress enough that you *must* respect everyone's personal space, boundaries, limitations, and possessions.

Bearing in mind, that Alters are as different as night and day, and that what might be fine with one may be objectionable to another, be careful of timing your visits as well. For example, always being cautious around "The Mean One's" bedroom may bode you well, especially, if he has had a bad day in the body, or a confrontation with someone inside for which he has not yet processed his anger. Likewise, an Alter who tends toward psychosis may be dangerous to your safety, if he or she is hallucinating or abreacting at the time you make your presence known. It is wiser to offer a simple "I'm here if you need me", and leave, than to stick your nose in where it is not welcomed.

The flip side of this coin, of course, is that you also have the right to walk about freely, sleep, hide, and even sit out in the open without another Alter intruding on your privacy. However, it is up to you to present your desire to be alone in a clear, polite manner. Sticking up for your rights, and those of your Alters, may initially be difficult. We know, we have been there a few times ourselves. However, each time you manage to do it and do it tactfully, you will be changing your negative scripts by empowering yourselves in positive communication. But, whatever happens, try to read the situation before tempers flare and things get out of hand. It is much better if you feel "out of sorts" to avoid contact and explain things later, and still be friends, then to become obnoxious and inconsiderate about respecting the personal space of your inner residents, taking months to repair good will.

Concurrently, it is in your best interest to advise your inner dwellers of any changes you have made in your own personal boundary regulations. Don't assume because you have changed your mind about your need for privacy, that "The General" who occasionally shares thoughts with you, has picked up on your new mind set. The safest way to proceed to avoid any misunderstanding, is to post a notice where all can see it (like at the main entrance to the body), or announce it at a "town meeting" (discussed in Chapter Five). That would also be an excellent time to resolve any conflicts or unfulfilled needs that may have arisen between yourselves.

Make sure when confronting another about a grievance, however, that it is a good time to do so and that there is always at least one person by your side. For example, if you know "The Gambling Addict" lost a lot of the family's funds playing poker last night, and that he has a "mad on" towards the world, don't set yourself up to receive his wrath by talking with him there and then. You may let him know you need to talk to him about something, but that you will come back later. However you decide to proceed, use good judgment, and be considerate and respectful of the other person's feelings.

Organizing Support Systems

One of the most rewarding benefits of deciding to work together as a family, is the inner support system you will create for yourself and your Alters. It is, undoubtedly, much easier to deal with the struggles and daily hassles of life when you have someone who you can rely on to wade through your troubles with you, and who values you, than to continue on in isolation. Many of us look outside ourselves for that support and are rudely disappointed when it is not forthcoming. We are in a unique category of survivors, often misunderstood even by sexual abuse survivors who are not Multiples, and find ourselves alone again without support when we are edged out of incest survivor support groups.

By building a strong, caring, constructive inner support group between you and your Alters, will assure that there is always someone available to listen and talk with you. Of course, you will not be the only one reaping the benefits. The children who may hold only a few good memories of their past, will relish the support and genuine caring of their new friends and family. Be careful to pay special attention to their needs. Though their needs may be very simple, ranging from wanting to be held, pushed on a swing, or wishing to be read to at night, it is important that they feel you are wholeheartedly invested in their lives. If they do not feel your total participation, it is quite possible that they will become easily manipulated by unruly or malicious Alters, who don't want or feel they deserve any "good" in their lives, and who are looking for any opportunity to crumble the family base.

Furthermore, as you get to know the Alters, all of them, you will start to put to memory important dates that are significant to one member or another. Jessie, for example, experiences intense pain around Easter because that is when her abuser first raped her. Sister Mary's constant praying around that time further upsets Jessie, because she feels God refused to answer her own prayers of rescue a very long time ago. As was true with Jessie, your Alters may be too deep into their misery to tell you what is going on with them, so, like remembering your own trigger dates, it is imperative that you remember your Alters' as well. It could mean the difference between a family member releasing their pain through tears, and releasing them with a razor blade. If necessary, mark off on a calendar the dates you need to remember.

Make yourself available during these difficult times to those who are hurting, and help them process their pain any way you can. Sometimes that involves nothing more than sitting with them, listening, holding their hands, or allowing them to cry. Subsequently, you my find that you, too, feel like crying. All the better for both of you. If you can genuinely empathize and cathart with them, you will put yourself on their level and validate their pain, while releasing some of your own distress. This also serves as encouragement to each other to explore healthy ways of releasing trauma. Crying really is not shameful. All well-adjusted people need to cry from time to time (despite what we may have been taught as children), to let out their pain so they can move on in their emotional and spiritual development.

Once a good support system is in place, it is our belief that you will be surprised at the decline of self-inflicted injuries to the body (we haven't had any in three years now), emotional blowups, and, overall, decrease in "acting out" or attention seeking behaviors.

Inner Sanctuary Building

Finally, there is a technique that you and your Alters can use to reduce tension, and provide yourselves with a peaceful retreat. Sanctuary building is done through "guided imagery" (the suggestion of therapeutic scenes, images, or interactions conducive to healing), and is a valuable art to be appreciated in working with survivors of terrible abuse.

Your sanctuary is a special niche that will be nicer and more practical, than a once a year vacation on a lush, tropical hideaway. If constructed properly, it will be a place you will visit often. A location where you can peacefully and safely meditate, dangle your feet in the cool waters of a babbling brook, or sleep uninterrupted on a bed of clover. A place, by the way, that is uniquely yours.

Alters who suffer from anxiety attacks, ulcers, and other medical infirmities are wonderful candidates for sanctuary building, as are paranoid types and children. This is a safe, individualized mental haven that is designed solely by the Alter, and is used exclusively by them, unless, of course, they want company. It is created out of bits of memory and imagination, and has no limits to what can be included. Children may need assistance in building a sanctuary, but don't tell them what they must include. Make suggestions only if they ask you for your input. Whatever a child Alter wishes to incorporate in this special setting, such as rabbits, swings, space ships, horses, sandboxes, or angels playing harps, so be it. The more comfortable and in control a person feels within their new space, the more they will readily use it when they are feeling troubled or overwhelmed.

Some Alters, especially the children, may need reminders to move themselves into their sanctuary during times of distress. Other Alters may need assistance and direction in getting themselves into their sanctuaries after they have already escalated into dysfunction, but make sure they understand your encouragement to go there is not a punitive measure. Obviously, it would be prudent for all concerned, if you intervene before they become too overwhelmed to go at all. However, never try to physically force them to go, as I have already suggested, or it may be experienced as punishment in their eyes and lose all calming benefits. Simply, remind them they do have a safe, quiet place they can retreat to where no one can bother them. If necessary, and if they wish it, agree to go there with them for a short time. (Working with dangerous Alters will be discussed in Chapter Six)

My sanctuary took sometime to construct, requiring many alterations and additions until I was completely comfortable and secure in feeling safe. When it was done it looked like this; nestled between two jagged snow capped mountain ranges, I placed a beautifully lush, green glade dotted with flowers of every kind, softly chirping birds, billowy white clouds that resembled animal shapes, and a secret entrance cut through rock that only I knew about. Twisting down out of the mountains, I envisioned and placed a stream that ran past my outstretched toes and wound its way down through a narrow opening in the rock to a placid, crystal clear lake below. The weather changed according to my needs, as did fragrances, and I often took a friend I trusted to lie with me in the soft grass under the warm, healing rays of the sun, while I utilized my relaxation and meditation techniques.

The time out and safety of my sanctuary suited my needs, as you can well imagine. Needless to say, positive results are very encouraging in the recovery process, which I, personally, experienced in the great reduction of panic attacks I was having on a daily basis.

We would like to note here, that some aspects of your mental sanctuary would benefit other members of your system such as swing sets for children, or a lazy river beside a big oak tree to reflect under, or a beautiful flower garden for withdrawn Alters to nurture. In these instances, we suggest you construct these healing special effects right within your system for everyone to access, which will make your inner environment much brighter and more functional. In addition, it will add some positive diversions for Alters who do not have much interaction with the outside world. Having pleasant surroundings to live in will help reduce the overall tension and frustration, when there is not enough meaning and activity that can be utilized through the use of the body.

My Inner Sanctuary

Memories of nature
I search in slumber
For a tranquil place
To hide from thunder.

Flowers, sky,
Whatever I choose
All that's beautiful
Is mine to use.

Within this sanctuary
I'm free to roam
Through lush, green grass
Or waves of foam.

Anger, worries,
Grief, and pain
Can't follow me there
I'm healed again.

Wouldn't you like
To build your own
Private retreat
To call your home?

You'll thank yourself
For a loving space
That's totally free
And always safe.

Chapter Two

Paving the Way Toward Unity

Letting Go of the Old Ways

The manner in which you and your Alters relate to the stressors in your lives, will be of paramount importance in determining how smoothly the building of your family structure will progress. Though each Alter has a reason and purpose for their existence, the old, unhealthy ways of doing business will no longer suffice as you begin to form a cohesive bond. For example, reverting to self-injurious behavior when being confronted with rejection, disappointment, or ridicule must be looked at by the Alter for what it truly is, nothing more than a hasty, self-defeating action which will keep them, and your system, in dysfunction. Though he or she might have vented their frustration temporarily, they didn't make anything better, only worse, perhaps, much worse for all.

An example of this is the way The Big Cutter (aka, Erick), when highly frustrated or angry, would bash our body's hands with a hammer, or repeatedly strike a sold object until the bones shattered beneath the force. Though he was free of *his* personal aggression following such an outburst, the body was wounded, often times to the point of requiring stitches and casts, and rendered us unable to work at our job. Needless to say, the weeks without work seriously jeopardized our financial security. Furthermore, his impulsiveness was the reason for many of our involuntary commitments to locked facilities. Once he recognized his behavior was not productive, and that his feelings could better be expressed by working them out on a heavy punching bag, or by talking privately with someone, things lightened up and he began to work on the issues that triggered his rages.

However, be prepared for some amount of resistance. Angry, protective, or frightened Alters may experience what you are asking them to do as a threat to their survival and purpose, and balk at your attempts to unify the members. Their hostility will be more difficult to work around, than say, the passive resistance you might receive from an indifferent Alter. Give them the wide berth they need, as they probably have more destructive memories and material that they are working off of. For example, memories of being forced to participate in Satanic rituals involving sacrifices and humiliation can hit deeper.

However, as you begin to set an example for the inner members by reshaping the way you think, and incorporating those new methods of coping into your daily existence and manner of relating to the other inner residents, eventually, even the more emotionally damaged persons will be observing your progress.

It is not easy to change a person's way of operating, but,

by being a good role model and demonstrating the effectiveness of your new attitude, you will find less resistance then you would by demanding they do something they are not completely comfortable with, nor have any experience of seeing someone else do.

For instance, "The Mean One" may need to see how the changes you have made in your way of thinking and responding to the outside and inside world, have been beneficial not only for the whole, but for you personally. He will want to know what he is going to get out of working on himself. Will he be manipulated by the others, or, will he be appreciated and treated in a fair and kind manner? Will his shift in demeanor make a big difference in getting his needs met, or, will his efforts be wasted? And, will he be respected by the others, or, will he be looked upon as a coward? He will have to process all of this before taking a risk in humiliating himself and joining your crusade.

Change does not come easy to anyone, and is particularly hard for survivors of severe abuse, especially those ritualistically abused. Often, Alters find themselves stuck in their inability to change the past, and therefore, continuously "act out" their old scripts in the present. This is especially true for teenage and young adult Alters. Jessie, for instance, when confronted by bad memories or the disapproval of others, resorted to her past behavior of doing drugs in order to cope. What's more, she would further detach from reality by refusing to hear what people were really saying to her, often rambling on about the stunts of her imaginary "Tree Monkeys". We found, that by being supportive of her pain and slowly teaching her how to talk about what was really bothering her, eventually, we were able to get her to react in a healthy productive manner instead of retreating into fantasy and delusion.

You, too, will have to lead some Alters by the hand until they realize that the danger they keep replaying has passed, and that it is safe to reshape their behavior to accommodate the needs of the inner community. Bear in mind, however, that this may take a long time for everyone to do, possibly even a lifetime, and cannot be rushed through. After all, It took them many years to develop into the people they are, and it will take many more to evolve into the helping, caring family members they will become.

Fortunately, it will not require every last Alter's participation before you experience love and harmony within your system. Undoubtedly, you will come up against some unruly, malicious Alters who will try to sabotage your efforts to incorporate the members. Respect where these Alters are coming from, but stand firm in your commitment to better your situation. Be patient and sympathetic to their fears of losing control. However, this does not mean you must lie down when they become nasty, or violent. Make it clear to them, from your collective, that their aggressive behavior towards anyone will not be tolerated, and that you will not communicate with them until they are able to process their anger in a civil manner. (If they are dangerous Alters, refer to Chapter 6.)

We know this can be effective in the long run, because Michael (a member of our system) was one of these combative types. Having grown up in a family that was always at each other's throats, he adopted the belief that he needed to be right all the time to avoid further confrontation or appear weak and stupid. Furthermore, he learned that in order to survive life with our abusers, he had to be ruthless and nasty. This was all that life was about for him. As you can probably imagine, this did not win him the favor of too many people. It wasn't until he joined in the effort to harmonize our group, that he came to understand the importance of letting go of his old patterns.

Once he understood the driving force behind his anger and lashing out, it became easier to let go of the past and deal with the here and now. This meant Michael had to learn about himself and accept the good along with the bad. He had to allow himself to be taught to communicate in a non-threatening, civil manner--something he, initially, felt very humiliated about doing. Finally, when he was able to let go of having to be right and in control all the time, he started "processing" his distress and concerns in a dignified way. Furthermore, he found himself able to accept criticism from others when it was presented in a kind, constructive manner, and his self-worth grew by leaps and bounds. In addition, the people who generally bore the brunt of his obnoxious, frequent "tongue lashings", actually started to like him and became willing to share more of themselves with him.

(We placed the word "processing" in quotes because we heard it so many times from Susan during our recovery, that we thought she might be pleased to see we really did pay attention to what she was trying so hard to teach us. Please excuse this slight digression, but we felt the need to publicly humble ourselves.)

Establishing Co-consciousness

Establishing co-consciousness means to become fully aware of your Alter's thoughts, feelings, issues, activities, and whereabouts much of the time, along with paying attention to important happenings in the outside world. Though it is not necessarily a requirement for becoming a well-adjusted Multiple, it is quite important in building a strong foundation for your emerging family.

By establishing co-consciousness, you will virtually stop the occurrences of "lost time", as well as gain a better understanding of the coping mechanisms and prevailing issues operating within each Alter person. This will also help you to establish alliances between yourself and your inner persons.

"So," you may ask, "how do I go about establishing co-consciousness?" The answer is simple, but also is difficult and time consuming. In a word, sharing, is the best way we know of to become an on-going part of each other's lives. The difficult part includes the sharing of past traumas, as well as the emotional aftermath, that has caused the unhealthy ways of relating to oneself and others. Things that make us feel bad have to be shared, just like things that make us feel good. When you think about it, wouldn't you like a family that would love you and help you when things are bad, just like they would react to you when things are good?

Unfortunately, most of your Alters were created to hide painful experiences and keep secrets from each other so that they could endure, in pieces, what happened to you as a whole. This was necessary at the time, because no single one of you could have endured it all. Now that most of you reading this are out of the hands of your abusers, or perhaps, have grown a big enough body so that you are not picked on as badly and can defend yourselves or get some help, its time to get well and start reorganizing your inner purposes for a life that you would like, and have the right to lead.

The mind shift should be from, merely, staying alive and handling torment, to rebuilding an inner structure conducive to peace and safety. Once the threats are removed from the outside, you need to get the word around your system that things have changed and you don't have to be afraid of certain people outside hurting you, nor your inner persons. Now that things are much safer, you need to get to know each other, grieve for each other, and rebuild together for a better inner world, one you, ideally, would have liked to grow up in.

Getting this word out and having people trust that it is true, will take a long time as there is likely a lengthy history of mistrust and betrayal to overcome. However, sharing with each other, rather than running away and hiding in fear, will get you started on the right track much quicker. Therefore, be prepared to accept and know about each other's memories after you become acquainted.

In truth, you all share in the energy and soul of your system, and developing insight and understanding will be much faster (and automatic for some Alters) as you begin communicating your feelings and experiences. The more time you share together in joint activities, the more co-conscious you become. This is particularly true when sharing space within the body. Having such close contact in a shared space, will allow you to experience the body and reactions to outside stimuli by each of you immediately. Initially, you may only have a vague sense of what the other is thinking and feeling, but if you keep this up, soon enough, you will be dialoguing through your every move together. It is only a matter of time until more of your persons share space in the body and can dialogue together as well. Then you will notice an almost telepathic ability start to occur between you whether you are sharing space, or even in sight, or not near each other at all.

You will also notice that those Alter persons who act like outsiders by remaining detached from the whole, generally, do not have the ability to share in this telepathic communication. In essence, co-consciousness is really opening up to each other, a task particularly difficult, because it requires trust and a willingness to allow yourself to experience love and pain.

Building Trust Among Family Members

Most Alters will have great difficulty trusting anyone, and justifiably so. However, If you have been successful in establishing co-consciousness, you will have learned a lot about their secrets and pain. In doing so, you will have laid the necessary ground work in preparing to help your Alters learn to trust you, and each other.

It is crucial to respect, however, that each Alter is unique and will require your patience and understanding in this process. Remind yourself that "Rome wasn't built in a day" and you will make surprisingly steady progress. Encourage each one to express how they are feeling about the changes that are taking place, and validate their concerns. No one likes to be laughed at or criticized when working on matters of such importance as learning a new social skill, so, "bite your tongue" if you have to hide your reactions for the sake of the family.

After awhile, they will begin to confide in you comfortably. They may even start to view the outside world in a whole different light. That is when you know that the changes in the way you are relating to them is truly working. As each Alter relies more, and more, on the family cohesiveness, it will be an indication that it is time to move on to the next step of planning for your collective futures.

Negotiating Time Restraints in Realizing Goals

As you, and your family, begin to "cast off" the ways of the past and rally around your efforts to unite, you will need to identify the long and short term goals of the individuals and the family as a whole. Accept, from the start, that this will be as difficult as it was getting to know the makeup of each Alter in the beginning. For, as many active people as there are in your system, so, too, are the number of personal desires for fun and fulfillment. Each one will have varied interests, hobbies, and duties that will be as important in their eyes as yours are to you.

For example, the "Inner Therapist" may have a burning desire to enroll in college full time so she can work toward getting a degree in psychology. This is her right as a contributing member of your family. However, as admirable as her goal may be, she may have failed to consider how desperate the family's finances are at this time, and that your first priority is to support the family by maintaining your day time job.

So, what are your alternatives? By discussing the matter with her in a mutually respectful manner, the "Inner Therapist" comes up with another idea. What if she enrolls in one or two night classes? Sure, that might work into your time frame restrictions, but how would it resolve the financial restraints? Well, maybe you can offer to help her with tuition at the start, providing she agrees to take it upon herself to first investigate the possibility of getting financial aid or student loans. Wonderful! She gladly accepts and everything is worked out, right? Well, probably not. Though attending night classes might be acceptable to your schedule, will not be a burden on the family's pocketbook, and won't interfere with "The Mother's" preparation of dinner, or "Little Sally's" art instruction which she attends at the local High School every weekend, it might very well conflict with "Eddie's" Tuesday night substance abuse recovery meeting. Rescheduling will likely solve the problems, but you will have to put forth effort to investigate these realities beforehand and establish priorities.

For your family to run smoothly, everyone's needs must be considered before an individual plan, or goal, can adequately be addressed and realized. By establishing who needs and wants what, you will avoid potential hazards of time and money restraints, as well as justifiable upsets within your system.

Once we worked this major scheduling issue out, we seldom had problems around an Alter's feelings being hurt, or plans being disrupted, and actually found the time to spend together in pursuit of family goals. Remember, never take another person for granted or expect them to, simply, give into you, and you will find negotiating the obstacles to be a lot less frustrating.

Another means of fulfilling needs and realizing goals is to

evaluate what desires can be accommodated within the system, versus, those that can only be achieved within the body in the physical world. The old saying that the mind has unlimited potential is particularly true when it comes to Multiples. They can create, virtually, any environment they want.

If "Susie" has always loved animals and dreamed of being a veterinarian, then a petting zoo can be created out of the mind's energy, just like Alters and living quarters are. If "Pete" longs for wide open spaces, or living in the woods, he can create that scenery for his living area inside which, seemingly, can stretch out for miles.

However, if "Martha" or "John" wish to start a newsletter to help survivors, or wish to become lawyers to prosecute perpetrators, they will have to plan to go to college and purchase a computer in physical life as their means to make an impact on the world.

As you can see, many of your goals can be accomplished within your system, and others will require greater planning, finances, and regulated use of the physical body.

"Rap" M.P.D.

Frag-men-tation
Dis-so-ci-ation
Tell me, where am I to go?
In-te-gration
Har-mon-ization
Too many names to know!

I-den-ti-ties
Person-a-li-ties
I'm an Alter, in someone else's head
Conclusion? Delusion!
In all my confusion
I think I'd be better off in bed!

Psychogenic fugue
My therapist came unglued
The First Born freaked and had to fade
The Host is a ghost?
But him I trusted most
Is Mercury or what in retrograde?

Bad ab-reaction
I'm now in traction
Flash-backs, switching, losing time
Suspicion, jokes, and leers
From everyone who hears
Is having M.P.D. a federal crime?

We The People
The Alter's
Bill of Right's
ISH

Chapter Three

Working Together for the Common Good

Assigning an Inner Self Helper

When you have adequately established a working trust between yourself and your Alters, it is time to assign an Inner Self Helper, if your system does not already have one, to facilitate the growth process of all the members. Doing this will free up your time to attend to other matters, while empowering individual Alters to continue in their development of group dynamics.

The Inner Self Helper (I.S.H.) will be responsible for advising the members in areas concerning personal growth issues and family matters, and to intervene in times of crisis. The I.S.H. should be an Alter from the protective branch, if possible, as these persons usually are thoroughly familiar with the strengths and weaknesses of the system, and hold a lot of information about the Alters and the abuse they endured.

Of course, everyone should be encouraged and allowed to add their input on the designation of this person. Do not assume that because some members are very old, very young, or not very active that they won't want to vote on this very important appointment. Run your family like a democracy and include everyone in the decision making process, no matter how silly their suggestions may sound. This will spare a lot of hurt feelings and establish a sense of importance for all the persons, even if the person selected wasn't their choice. To have one's opinions considered elicits good feelings, even if their comments or suggestions are not part of the final product.

For example, if four year old "Lulu" thinks the family pet should be the Inner Self Helper, don't ridicule or laugh at her. Discuss with her how that may or may not be in the best interest of all concerned, validate her, thank her for her input, and move on to the next person. "Lulu" will feel good for having her contribution considered and so will you for having included her. In addition, the support and respect you show her will encourage her to continue thinking about the good of the group, and influence her thinking about ways she can improve her own behavior and consideration towards others.

You should further keep in mind, that the most assertive of your Alters may not necessarily be the best person for the job either. They may have a tendency to assert too much control over individuals' decisions, thus causing strife among the members. A compassionate, even dispositioned Alter might be better for this position. However, all of you must choose this person as carefully, if not more so, as Americans elect a president. Find out where the perspective I.S.H. stands on issues involving the inner persons' recovery, and how much of themselves they are willing to invest toward that end. Remember to place "principles over personalities", and you should be able to decide on the best person for the job. Once you, as a group, decide who that person will be, all of you need to agree to cooperate with the I.S.H.'s intentions and respect their position in matters of arbitration. This means you may not get what you want in terms of an outcome during a dispute, but, that you agree to abide by the decision of the I.S.H. and trust that your needs will be taken into consideration. After all, it is possible for you, or anyone, to be wrong, or that you could have handled things differently.

Constructing an Alters' Bill of Rights

The first official duty of the family's newly appointed Inner Self Helper should be to assist your inner residents in drawing up an Alter's Bill of Rights. This document should cover the basics such as trust, rights, responsibilities, consequences, and any bylaws the members agree are necessary to ensure that no one's rights are abused or violated, and should be signed by each person. As I have stated before, the more Alters feel that they have a say in what happens in their community, the more empowered they will become, and the more they will want to work with the group and on their individual issues.

A sample of an Alter's Bill of Rights might look something like this:

Preamble: We, the members of (so and so's) inner family, in order to establish a cooperative, healthy, working relationship among us and a strong foundation for recovery, hereby, adopt these rules and regulations as our official agreement concerning the rights and responsibilities to be afforded each member, and honored by us all.

1. Each inner person must take responsibility for his own actions and issues.

2. At no time will physically aggressive behavior toward another family member be tolerated unless it is, clearly, an act of self-defense or protection.

3. Alters agree that the concern for the safety of the body must always be considered before the desires or needs of the individual.

4. Alters are responsible to report to the I.S.H. any behaviors in themselves, or other Alters, that may be interpreted as potentially dangerous to the preservation of the whole, as soon as they become aware of them. The I.S.H. and appropriate members are to help, not judge, such Alters in therapeutically addressing the problem.

5. Alters have a right to have their grievances heard and addressed in a fair and timely fashion.

6. Violent, dangerously out of control, suicidal, or homicidal Alters, will be placed in a safe, confined space until they are able to regain composure and make amends if they have insulted or harmed anyone.

7. Alters willfully disrespecting the rights of anyone (such as bullying or malicious manipulation to undermine the inner stability), will be subject to disciplinary action by a review board, selected by the Alters or guardian in charge and the Inner Self Helper.

8. Any person(s) who willfully, and repeatedly, conspire to destroy other Alters, or participate in Satanic activities, or endanger the safety of "the system" such as indiscriminate unsafe sex (i.e., possible exposure to AIDS),

or to law enforcement through criminal or violent behavior, while refusing to adhere to the consequences determined appropriate by the review board, are, therefore, subject to permanent confinement or rendered inactive.

9. Each inner person has a right to formulate and maintain loving relationships with each other (who are in agreement), and will respect "couples", special friendships, family roles, and pets within the system.

10. Inner persons have a right to personal property and private living quarters (area) to decorate and use as they see fit. Living quarters and personal items are not to be invaded or taken by others, unless by permission, and communal property is to be shared.

This is only a partial example of what your family's bylaws may resemble. It is up to the collective to decide how involved and detailed to make it. Having been abused, and, or, dismissed by so many people in our lives, we found that grounds rules were key in helping our system to achieve a cohesive, trusting bond. However, your system may unanimously agree that a Bill of Rights is not needed. That is your prerogative, but it is not advised. Like a winning baseball team, some order should be established, if for nothing else, to diminish self-destructive behavior.

Redefining Alters' Roles Within Your System

Once you have set down some rules, or determined how your system will run most efficiently, you can further unite the members by helping the Alters to find new meaning or purpose for themselves within their community. As most Alters were born to handle specific, distressing, or awkward situations, it would be unreasonable to assume they would give up their scripts, simply, because you requested them to. Furthermore, stripping them of their roles without developing new ones ahead of time is very invalidating, and could trigger negative reactive behaviors that could be detrimental to your recovery. Like the process of retraining a disabled or unemployed person, you will have to help them to identify their individual strengths and weakness so that they can realize a new, productive value for themselves within your system.

Grizzly, for example, one of my more colorful Alters, had always been responsible for assuming executive control of the body when it was in physical pain or distress. For many years, he walked about with broken bones and serious injuries without feeling any pain. Though this seemed beneficial at the time, as we started to unite ourselves we came to realize that because Grizzly did not experience the body's distress, he inadvertently caused it more harm by running it so ragged that it was unable to heal properly. Retraining him meant helping him to understand, that though his services were crucial for so many years, and that we appreciated his efforts, it was time for the body to process its pain and begin to heal. Surprisingly, as he accepted this truth, he began to feel the body's discomfort and limitations the same as everyone else.

"So, what's so great about that?" you might ask. "We don't want to feel anymore pain." Well, we can certainly relate to that style of thinking. However, in order to keep the family on an even keel, it is necessary to help the body heal from the trauma of the past. I am not merely referring here to accidental injuries, but to the emotional trauma the body stores in its cells as negative energy when we stuff down feelings about our experiences. Modern medicine is confirming in their studies that damage from stored emotional trauma is not merely an assumption, but an actual physical phenomenon within all humans. In fact, there are professionals called "Rebirthers" who help clients to release these trapped traumas from birth.

Once Grizzly admitted his role was in need of reworking, we helped him to assess his character strengths and talents which could be put to good use. Thus, we were successful in giving him back a sense of renewed purpose within our system. In addition, because of Grizzly's inability to read and write, and his heavy, gruff, and nasal New York accent, we decided he was not the best Alter to assume responsibility for inquiring about benefits and filing papers with government agencies. However, we soon realized he had a "common man's genius" when it came to identifying and fixing mechanical problems, and that he could "jury rig" just about anything with minimum ease or expense, and make it work!

Needless to say, we decided he was, by far, the best suited and most knowledgeable person among us on matters pertaining to the maintenance of the car and household appliances. So, now, his job is to service the family automobile and fix things around the house, two things he has fun doing and has achieved great satisfaction from. In addition, he is one of the only Alters willing to do laundry and general housework, though he sometimes grumbles about it.

Less active Alters, such as children, will be more difficult to reassign duties. But, by using the method described above, you should be helpful in finding something which will give them new purpose and importance, and that they will enjoy. For example, they could be adopted by Alters who enjoy parenting and living as a family, or adding laughter and creativity to the system, taking care of inner pets, appreciating nature or flowers, being artistic, or most importantly, informing you when someone inside feels bad and needs your assistance.

The Importance of Validating Feelings

As your team adjusts to their new life-styles, and each other, you will have to make sure that they receive adequate praise for the efforts they put forth or the good work they are doing. For those of us who came from violent, abusive homes, it is understandable that we would have very few memories of our feelings or achievements being validated by anyone in our lives. Our abusers certainly did not validate how we felt, or they would not have done the things they did, nor did the church validate our needs or they would have intervened on our behalf. Similarly, we were misunderstood and made fun of by our peers in school, being called mean and derogatory names that crumbled our self-worth further, and invalidated our feelings all the more.

Names with negative associations and nicknames given us for weaknesses or behaviors that are humiliating, only keeps our spirits down and makes positive change impossible. It is important when changing one's self-concept from the inside, to also change our image through positive associations with which we wish to be recognized. Consequently, a revision of role and job description can be accompanied by a change in name or status, by which the group should abide. Allow each Alter to choose a name they feel proud of, and use it whenever addressing them in your communications.

It took a long time for our system to get to this point, but we now realize that nothing makes a person feel better about who they are and what they are doing, than to feel they are heard, appreciated, and recognized for their efforts and beliefs. Similarly, nothing makes a person give up trying faster than chronic invalidation or ridicule. This is especially true for the children Alters. Give them plenty of attention and listen to what they have to say, even if you don't agree with it.

Make periodic assessments to check if there are any major

flaws in the reconstruction of your system or the way you communicate with each other, and to see that all is running smoothly. Special effects, such as living quarters, pets, and natural settings are easy to add or rearrange. Undoubtedly, sometimes there are going to be disputes and animosity between Alters. Expect it and don't panic when it arises. There are ways of working things out. (Resolving conflicts will be discussed in Chapter 5)

What we have found in harmonizing ourselves, is that a lot of problems can be circumvented simply by validating the feelings of the members, and by making occasional minor adjustments. Do not let anyone "rag" on another or verbally tear them apart, and if you see it happening, "nip it in the bud" by invoking your collective "Bill of Rights" and the consequences you all agreed on ahead of time. As soon as Alters realize you mean business about protecting everyone's rights, including the meaner ones, mutual respect and trust will start to flourish. Just work at keeping everyone centered by using compassion, love, and dignity, and the atmosphere inside will lighten up considerably.

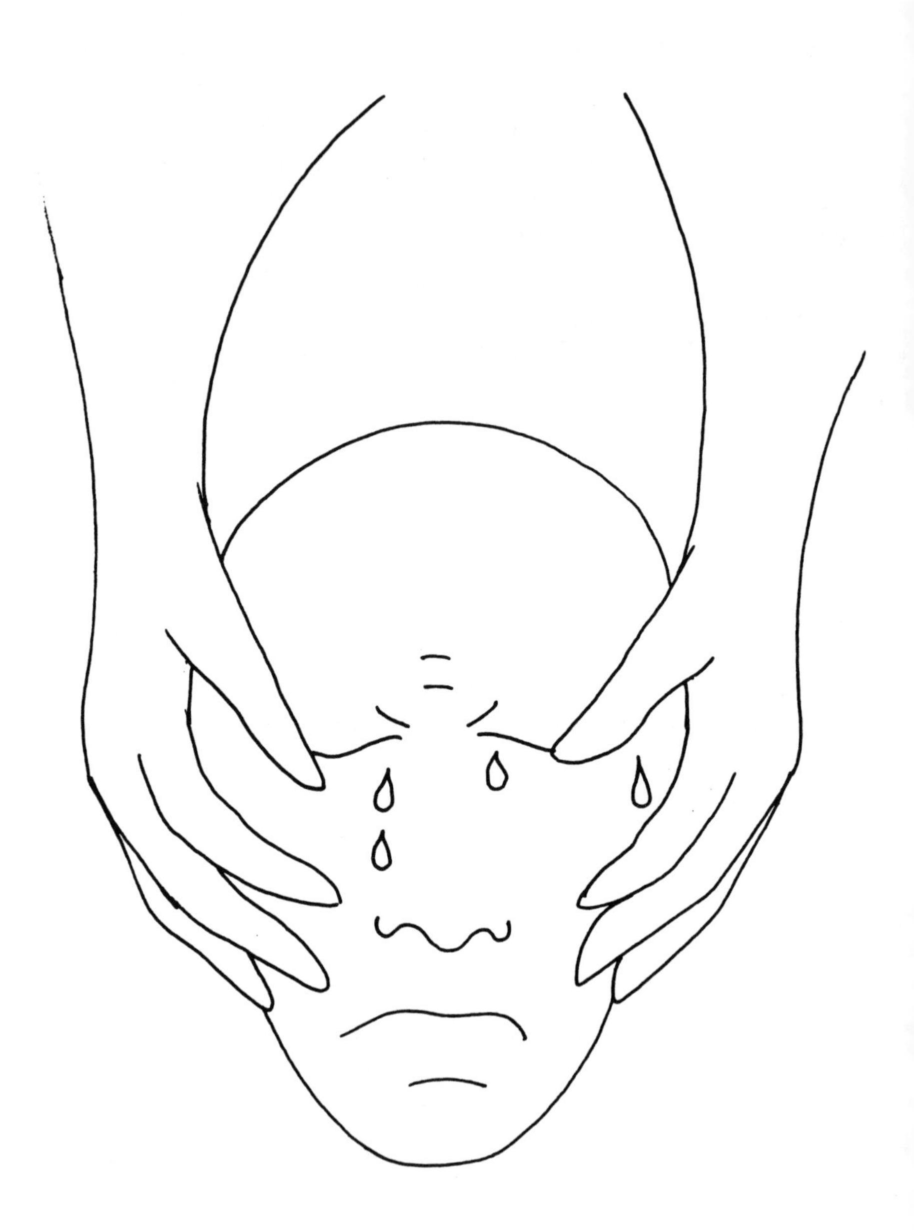

Chapter Four

Making a Collective Commitment to Therapy

The Necessity of a Therapeutic Process

Just as a new automobile needs ongoing tune-ups, oil changes, tire rotations, etc. to stay in peak operational condition, so, too, do your family members need therapeutic support. To manage your evolving family effectively, it will be important for all of you to seriously begin dealing with the memories and issues that have, for so many years, held you in dysfunction. You would not expect your car to make it across country without oil to lubricate its parts, the engine would surely blow up. The same correlation can be drawn concerning Alters' needs for appropriate outlets for their frustration, pain, and concerns. To simply perform a job or function is one thing, to become healthy and well-adjusted is quite another.

In getting to know all about the minds within you (as covered in chapter 1), you probably (I hope) took mental notes about who had what issues to work on. Now is the time to encourage them to take steps toward resolving their residual pain, traumas, and resentments.

For Multiples who have had bad experiences with therapists, hospitals, etc. there will be a natural inclination toward resistance around the suggestion that the family members commit to therapy. However, "therapy" in this context does not imply that you *must* place your complete trust in a professional therapist. Though some aspects of your healing and unification would be more effectively handled by such a person, it is not impossible to facilitate your own growth through means of *self-directed* healing. This method was the crux of our healing experience, and can be adapted to fit your individual needs. We will, however, try to point out the benefits, and shortcomings, of all the professional options mentioned in this chapter.

The Therapeutic Options Available to You

There are many types of professionals, para-professionals, and agencies available to assist and direct you in your recovery. We will briefly discuss the ones we are familiar with to help clarify what the focus of each is.

Psychologists are Ph.D's (i.e, licensed doctoral graduates), who offer different treatment perspectives depending on the theory of dysfunction that the clinician is trained in. They usually work with one or some combination of the four forces in psychology (Psychoanalysis, Behaviorism, Humanism, and Cognitive), to therapeutically restructure, or dismantle, human dysfunction so that the person can achieve a healthy relationship within themselves and with others. They are trained to delve into deep rooted abnormal pathologies from early childhood, that lend themselves toward chronic dysfunction.

The most common of these forces used to treat abnormal development is psychoanalysis or Freudian depth psychology. This explores the impact of family dynamics, environmental stimuli, and parenting on the developing drives, ego, and associated cognitive functions of infants, children, and adolescents. It also examines behavioral and subconscious coping strategies in how you got your needs filled, as well as how your family manipulated you to fill their needs. However, it doesn't address healing. It, mostly, addresses understanding or insight believing that once this is achieved, the person will automatically change.

Another traditional profession of abnormal pathologies are psychiatrists. These are medical doctors (M.D.'s), who generally perceive dysfunction as likely to be the result of chemical imbalances and malfunction within the brain and central nervous system, in addition to poor parenting and environmental support. Furthermore, they believe if they can manipulate your inner perception through the use of medications, by creating an inner environment of stability and mental clarity, you will be more amenable to reasonable thinking and acting, and advancement in a therapeutic relationship. Unfortunately, as most of you already know, medications have limited effects on Alters who have so many different constitutions, and who are not always present in the body to absorb the medication and receive the benefit.

Master's level counselors consist of L.C.S.W.'s (Licensed Clinical Social Worker), L.I.C.S.W's (Licensed Independent Clinical Social Worker), and M.S.W.'s (Masters of Social Work). These clinicians deal primarily with social development, motivation, coping strategies, and interpersonal social skills in the workplace and personal relationships. However, they are *not* well-trained in the deeper abnormal pathologies or ego development under severe trauma. Their primary goal is to stabilize you, get you functioning, and networked with the appropriate agencies, social services, groups, etc., so that your basic survival needs are being met. They generally limit their treatment to short term therapy within clinics and hospital settings under the supervision of an M.D., unless they are in private practice. This is because insurance only covers limited stays for certain problems in residential facilities, and limited care in out-patient clinics. Furthermore, the volume of patients constantly being added within their facilities, drains the staff of quality time afforded to individual care.

Other master's level counselors are M.F.C.C's (Marriage, Family, and Child Counselors), who explore the dynamics of family relationships and their impact on a given individual, be it an adult or child. They also study marital and relationship counseling among individuals and couples. Because of their family focus, they can explore developmental stumbling blocks and issues that are common among individuals. Also, in their training, they frequently handle supplemented forms of self-abuse and compulsions such as substance abuse, eating disorders, etc. As in the prior category, they are not well trained in attending to deep rooted severe pathologies resulting from chronic childhood abuse or organic imbalances.

In contrast, non-traditional psychology incorporates experiential techniques and treatment specialties learned outside the academic setting, and can include transpersonal (i.e., spiritual) perspectives in healing. An experiential clinician's primary focus is in utilizing techniques that enhance a client's self-exploration and discovery of one's own growth process, connecting to traumatic life experiences through emotional catharsis, subjective interpretation of key experiences, and how the client wishes to apply these subjective realizations into their life and behavior. Transpersonal clinicians go further by encouraging the client in the mastery of self-directed healing techniques, to create out of *their own* inner resources (which may be untapped) abilities to heal themselves physically, mentally, and spiritually resulting in autonomy. The end result is not only to find important meaning in one's life (bad as it might have been), but to establish new purpose, broaden their vision, and strengthen themselves spiritually.

Some specialty techniques in non-traditional therapy include clinicians trained in hypnosis, psychodrama, gestalt, rebirthing, past life therapy, some substance abuse programs, inner child work, art therapy, psychosynthesis, body work, sand tray, special education, meditation, etc.. These specialties may require limited degrees or none at all, though many of them require a master's degree. They are trained under specialists of certain techniques and may have a letter of certification, like a drug dependency counselor, but work primarily in private practice. Few of these offer background education in addressing the psychosocial dynamics forming severe pathologies or their development, but these experiential methods may benefit someone with a severe pathology more than traditional forms of therapy as they are more creative.

It is important to note that any licensed professional, counselor, or specialist can, on their own, learn a great deal about a particular population or pathology, and specialized treatments that could address your needs quite well. So, read resource directories and articles by specialists, or talk with local therapists, to see where their interests, experience, and special education lie.

Bear in mind, that there are many branches of psychology and psychiatry, and the approach a clinician takes will be dependent upon their orientation, personal beliefs, and interests. Before deciding on a treatment specialist, you should find out as much about their treatment and the person themselves as possible. Since you are paying for their services, you have a right to know what their psychological orientation is, what their attitudes are regarding multiplicity and treatment, and if they have a religious agenda they utilize in treatment. You may also do well to investigate other treatment specialties and search for a professional that does the one(s) you want.

When looking for a professional, we suggest you develop a questionnaire beforehand, with such questions as, "How much prior experience have you had working with multiples? What is your treatment plan or approach? Do you believe integration is *necessary* for a person to be functional and well adjusted, and, is this your only method of cure? What are your treatment perspectives in cases of ritual abuse?" Sometimes a client doesn't find out they were ritually abused until much later, and requires a whole new level of understanding by a therapist which can activate their fear, or a religious or personal agenda that does not agree with you.

When speaking with a potential therapist, watch for indications of their being open to what you have to say and how they value your input. Ask them if they view multiplicity to be the primary problem that needs curing, or do they understand that it is the trauma from a severely abusive childhood that needs to be reprocessed and healed? How long do they anticipate you will need to participate in therapy, and how many times a week? And, find out if they are affiliated with a hospital that has a dissociative unit in the event you need short term crisis stabilization. If so, does he/she know the hospital's approach to treating Multiples? But, most importantly, don't forget to inquire if they have the proper amount of time in their schedule (you will do best with extended sessions several times a week), their policies around boundaries and emergency/crisis off schedule care, and enthusiasm to work with tough cases requiring a lot of personal investment? Of course, you may have important questions of your own to add to the questionnaire, such as their personal management of Alters whether adult or child, dangerous or unruly, or ones who act out sexually, as well as their personal extent of tactile contact (children alters need affection).

Circulate your questionnaire to the various professionals you are considering as potential allies in your recovery. Any therapist who is "worth his salt" will be happy to answer your questions, seeing them as a healthy first step in your recovery process. Those who refuse to respond or call you back, are making an unconscious statement that either they don't believe in your diagnosis, they don't want or need your business, or that they don't have the time, patience, or knowledge to deal with cases like yours.

Once you receive the questionnaires back, have your inner family members analyze the respondents answers thoroughly. Did the respondent say he believed integration was necessary to be well-adjusted, or that it was their only method of cure? If so, he or she may be working from outdated material, is inflexible, or, simply, has never worked with such a client. Did he or she say they were familiar with other methods such as harmonized co-existence, or partial integration, and that the choice was up to you? Did they have a religious orientation to treatment that was comfortable with you?

You will be able to gage from their responses and openness to you, whether this person is an appropriate professional to assist you. Don't set yourself up, or your family, to be disappointed by another well-intentioned but limited therapist. Find out right from the start if the person has enough qualifications (in cases of insurance, the company may require licenses and specific credentials), the right kind of specialized training for your treatment and needs, experience working with similar clients, and if they don't, are they open, or limited, in their ability to experiment in therapy?

Self-directed Healing

As I have stated before, it is entirely possible for you to

direct your own healing. This can be done through extensive reading about your condition(s), attending local workshops, regional conferences, and therapist facilitated support groups, or a combination of self-help groups such as A.A, Co-dependency, Overeaters Anonymous, Adult Children of Alcoholics, or M.P.D./D.D. meetings. Another aid would be to purchase self-directed healing tapes from survivor organizations (Dr. Shore has three tapes available for this purpose titled *"Healing Meditations and Inner Sanctuary Building for Survivors, Multiples, and Their Alters"*, *"Establishing Co-Consciousness and Cooperation Among Alters During Abreactive Experiences"*, and *"Breaking Down the Lingering Power of Abusers Through Reframing and Inner Child Work"*. Details for ordering these tapes are located in the appendix at the back of this book).

You may decide you only need a case manager, or social worker, to assist you with networking, make weekly home support visits, or to admit you to hospitals during times of unmanageable crises. One or more of your Alters may only need medication. If so, make it clear to the psychiatrist you choose that *you* will be directing and managing your own therapeutic recovery, and that you only require his assistance in areas of medication. If he cannot accept this, you may want to move on to someone else. People have controlled and manipulated your life for a very long time. There's no time like the present for self-empowerment. We realize, however, that even though self-empowerment is what most survivors inwardly want and strive for, there still may be some who are too frightened and dependent on "the system", or too dysfunctional to manage safely on their own. If this is the case, do whatever you have to in the way of outside support, until you reach a point in your recovery where you can start to stand on your own two feet.

To reiterate, find out by any means you can, all about your condition and how others have been helped. Attend workshops and conferences, if you can afford them, or do a work/attendance exchange. Take only those parts of what you need, or learn, that agrees with you and try them out, and put "on a back burner" those things which you are not sure will help you at this time. Take an inventory of the needs of your Alters, designate their new roles and responsibilities, and enlist the aid of the Inner Self Helper to coordinate their efforts and dialogue with everyone on their issues. It really is okay to try your own ideas. Keep in mind solutions that will benefit the whole, and contract with your Alters toward that end.

Finally, work on finding ways to release your pain and rage non-harmfully, such as exercise, boxing your mattress, or destroying objects representing your abusers. Immerse your selves completely in your recovery process. Do this through artwork, daily journaling, and subscribing to survivor newsletters and support groups. Also, you might consider becoming active by joining grassroots organizations that are committed to helping survivors, or who's goals are to educate society about the devastation child abuse causes. You will be amazed at the good feelings and sense of purpose taking up a cause will cultivate in your soul.

Remaining Open to New Experiences

A common stumbling block for anyone endeavoring to change themselves, or their situation, is often their inability to remain open to new experiences and alternative techniques of healing. Although you were deeply conditioned to be cynical and mistrusting at a very early age, if stability and recovery is foremost in your mind, you must make a pledge to yourselves to try everything that is affordable (even if it is strange), and consider anything that is morally sound and has potential, at all, in helping you to achieve your goals. You may be laughed at for some of the methods you will eventually try, or may even be discouraged by friends, family, and professionals who think you've "gone over the edge". But, when it comes down to choosing between apples or carrots, it's a matter of what *your* system can tolerate and not what will placate others.

Take it upon yourself to investigate all your options by gathering as much information about them as you can. Ask other survivors and friends what helped them the most, and then evaluate everything on its merits individually, step by step. Throw out or put aside what you cannot use, but most importantly, don't dismiss something, simply, because it sounds "too weird" to you. Consider the treasures that would have been lost if no one had opened that first oyster to find a precious pearl growing inside. And, what about the Wright Brothers and their flying machine? Everyone laughed at them for their ridiculous contraption which people were sure would never fly. Had they been intimated or swayed by other's criticisms, it is quite likely they would never have developed the airplane. However, they persisted in what they needed to do for themselves despite the ridicule and scorn, and, eventually, were successful.

The same analogy can be applied from blades of grass and hollow reeds to woodwind instruments, or the discovery of penicillin from common bread molds. Do what you need to do for you, and don't let yourself be influenced by well-meaning friends who are frightened of untried or unproven methods. After all, isn't it wiser and more desirable to be healed by an unorthodox method of therapy, than to remain ill in a program that is obviously inadequate for your needs?

For example, I always thought acupuncture was a waste of time and money. Furthermore, I firmly believed that people who put their faith in oriental herbal shysters had some subconscious need to continue being exploited. However, when we became seriously ill two years ago, with a disease for which there is no cure, we tried everything we could think of, or that was suggested to us, to relieve the torturous, debilitating pain we experienced on a daily basis.

It is interesting the things you will try when you're in enough pain that you just don't care how silly you look, or what other people think about you. Acupuncture and homeopathies were two of those things for us. However, they worked better than conventional methods, and were relatively painless despite what I had anticipated. Very fine needles, placed strategically in key points along meridian lines (energy flow lines throughout the body), pulled trapped energy away from inflamed, painful areas and organs causing relief of my symptoms. In addition, the unblocking and recirculating of the "life force energy", along with re-stabilizing homeopathics, stimulated my immune system to start healing itself. Amazing what can happen when we transcend our cultural conditioning.

The same is true with chiropractics. Many years ago the general population, and certainly the medical establishment, thought chiropractics was nothing more than a bunch of inadequately educated doctors out to make a fast buck. However, with medical costs skyrocketing, and advancements in treatment of sports injuries through chiropractics and homeopathic solutions, Americans are seeking alternative courses of treatments to help them. As a result, people are finding they are gaining considerably quicker relief, and even cures, from non-traditional forms of medicine.

Learn to accept that everyone has differences in their approach to dealing with life, and that ***all*** of us are really only experimenting with an unknown outcome anyway. Don't try to change anyone else, that is not your job. Just stay focused on your own goals, and respect that not everyone is going to agree with you, be it a professional or another survivor. Also, recognize that there isn't a single method that is going to solve all your problems. Just like many different doctors are required to take care of all your varied health needs, many different therapeutic aids may be required to help you in your recovery.

For ten years on the East Coast, I tried unsuccessfully to resolve my inner turmoil of pain and rejection, find the reason for my repeated failed attempts at life, and to mold myself into a traditional therapeutic framework which was inadequate for my needs. Needless to say, I did not make, or maintain, any substantial progress. When I moved to the West Coast, however, I was exposed to a whole different world of therapeutic interventions. Some I thought were pure quackery, while others seemed like things I could find some value in. As I learned to stay open to the various orientations and interests of practitioners, I soon realized that even the approaches I believed were quackery had something to offer me in my recovery. It was then that I began my quest to heal mentally, emotionally, and spiritually regardless of what that entailed. In three years time, myself, and my Alters, have achieved a harmonious co-existence that ten years of traditional therapy with L.C.S.W.'s and psychiatrists were unable to provide. This does not mean that traditional therapy is not right for others, I just use this example to support my statement of the necessity of remaining open to new experiences. Remember, to choose for yourselves what you wish to try, and that "what is one man's trash, is another man's treasure."

Also, remind yourselves that at any point along a therapeutic track or technique in healing, that it is always a Multiple's prerogative to change their minds if it does not seem to be working out for you. Approach everything you try as an *experiment* in order to bypass the self-limiting scripts around the words failure and mistakes.

I'd like to make a special note here to therapists working with Multiples. We receive numerous phone calls and letters everyday from distressed M.P.'s who share with us their concerns and displeasure with some professionals who do not validate their children Alters. We understand many of you are trying to put these people back together by using standard clinical techniques you were taught, which may discourage regression and personal contact, focusing more on the day to day functioning of the "Host". From experience, I can tell you this is not the best way to proceed. Children Alters are very real, needy, and will impede the therapeutic process if not encouraged to participate as themselves. If you have been around infants and toddlers in your own life, you would have noticed that adult communication is lost on them. They communicate through touch and physical senses. Therefore, appropriate nurturing contact through their bodies will tell them if you are safe and someone they can trust. They also make better use of toys, dolls, and objects to show you what happened to them because words fail them.

As compassionate humans, and as professionals who have witnessed a lot of pain in their careers, I encourage you to try to understand these people (M.P.'s) as unique and atypical individuals, who will probably never be perceived by society as "normal". Work at understanding ***their*** systems and goals to build a strong foundation, before jumping in with both feet with the intention of dismantling it. This means getting down on the floor and hugging "Little Darling", spending the whole therapy session drawing pictures with them, or using your imagination to mentally venture inside their systems if they are amenable to showing it to you.

For example, you will get no where talking English to someone who doesn't understand the language. You either learn their dialect, or waste precious time and energy trying to make them understand you through hand gestures. With Multiples, we suggest that you try to envision the persons within. You do not have one complex adult patient that you are working with, and you must get involved with who, and why, each of them are there. By working within their systems, as ***they*** experience it, you will bypass a lot of stumbling blocks and resistance. And, you will be surprised by the real progress you make in a relatively short period of time.

I realize you may initially feel foolish, or shunned by your colleagues for your unorthodox approach, but, please, don't let history repeat itself by betraying your patients the way Freud did when the pressure was put on him. The results you achieve by daring to be different and working within a Multiple's system using their realities, will cancel out the negative responses you get from your profession. After all, isn't the recovery of the client the most important part of the therapeutic process? And, shouldn't recovery be measured in ***their*** happiness rather than your standing in the professional community?

Of course I care, and want to talk to each of your Alters!

Thank's Doc. See you Friday!

Chapter Five

Processing Dissatisfaction and Resolving Disputes

Be Prepared for Conflict

I, personally, have never known or heard of a family that didn't have a fight or periodic argument over one thing or another. Disputes are as much a part of family life as colds or economic slumps are to our country. No one, despite how well-mannered and even dispositioned he might be, is immune from relationship discord. Furthermore, in my opinion, to elevate oneself or family to that realm of thinking is setting oneself up for major disappointment and embarrassment. We are ***all*** human and fallible.

Understand, there will be times when no one in your system agrees, and times when you will absolutely hate each other due to conflicts and differences. It is inevitable, but it does not mean the end of the wonderful work you are doing together, it just may be a sign that someone needs some time out. In fact, depending on how you wish to view it, disharmony could be considered as merely a "crisis of healing", or exposing a hidden problem that can now be appropriately addressed. If you promptly address the persons' complaints in a fair, compassionate fashion, the persons involved will have the opportunity to learn and grow from their experience and see one another in a more humane light. Resolving conflict amicably, instead of demanding our own way, allows us to grow in our understanding of the other person's needs, while lending maturity to our own development. Furthermore, each time you are successful in orchestrating a peaceful resolution to a conflict between you and your members, you are overcoming a little more of the negative conditioning you learned as a child.

We have included, below, some methods that worked well for us. However, like the rest of the suggestions in this book, they will need to be adapted and changed to accommodate your family's needs.

Using the Town Meeting Forum

Coming from a small town in New England, I am quite familiar and comfortable with the Town Meeting system used there for centuries. It is a democratic method of communicating the needs, desires, and interests of a town's citizens on issues of importance such as taxes, appointments of town officials, the creation of new bylaws, and the allocation of funds. This usually happens once a year, but for your specific needs, it may be wise to establish quarterly, or even monthly meetings (but don't be surprised if weekly meetings are needed in times of stress). More often is preferred when first starting out. Make sure a quorum is present (the number of members you decide must be present before you can discuss business) so as not to "step on anyone's toes" when making important decisions.

Myself, and my Alters, have patterned our process after these old New England ways, and have found it to be a cornerstone in our foundation. Thus, enacting such a Democratic process in our management has established an unspoken respect for each other's concerns. By calling a town meeting, we are able to process group dissatisfaction and disputes in a timely, and, generally, friendly manner.

Of course, the moderator of such a meeting is responsible for seeing to it that no one's feelings are recklessly disregarded in this process, and that even the youngest of residents have a chance to "take the floor" and be heard. By doing so, you validate each member, and that is what makes a system function adequately and peacefully.

It is important to establish a written agenda before the meeting starts, so that you are able to maintain order during the proceedings and to realize your group goals. You may wish to incorporate that the bylaws, or Bill of Rights, be read before the meeting begins, so that everyone present will be reminded of their "group spirit" and obligations as a participant.

Start the meeting by calling it to order, and then read the list or agenda that you have prepared. Try to arrange the list in an order reflecting the most prominent needs first. Then ask if anyone has anything they'd like to add to the list before you start discussing its contents, or any time constraints that a particular Alter has with items to be discussed before he or she has to leave. Also, set a time for breaks during the meeting for Alters to rest, walk around, and to think about the issues being discussed. Frequent breaks are important in keeping the attention of everyone in attendance, and provides upset Alters a "cooling off" period when dealing with heavy issues.

Make it a point to run the meeting in an orderly fashion, and delegate someone to be the "Sergeant at Arms" (a police officer of sorts) to restore order in the event that tempers flare to an unmanageable level, or to guide someone who is disruptive away from the meeting. This has happened with us, and having someone there to handle such problems establishes a sense of security for the younger and less assertive Alters.

Work the issues through in discussion, at least until most of the Alters are in agreement and satisfied with the resolution. This is usually indicated by their unanimous decision to vote on the motion or issue. For those things you are stalemated about, or are too tired to resolve at that time, select a committee to research the matter for their recommendations to the collective, and then "table" the discussions till your next meeting. Make sure, however, to follow-up on its resolution.

Convening a Council

There will be times when a town meeting of all members will be inappropriate. Such a circumstance might be when a conflict arises between only two members. If "John" and "Mike" are in dispute over the use of stereo time, it would not make sense to involve everyone. This would only further complicate everyone else's routines. If the two are unable to straighten out their differences in an amicable fashion, it will be necessary to convene a dispute council to help settle such inner conflicts.

This council of three to five members should be selected anew every few months, or so, if you have a large number of persons, to avoid an imbalance of power. Have the Alters present their respective cases to the board, which then considers a solution or compensation that can benefit everyone, if not soon, then in the near future.

For example, when we lived back in New England, there

was a problem between Grizzly and myself over excessive heating bills during the winter months. As head of the family, I got verbally upset with him, frequently, because we couldn't afford a hundred dollar gas bill each month. Then he, in turn, would yell at me claiming I was trying to freeze him to death. Finally, setting aside our differences on what temperature the thermostat should be set at, we took our dispute to our Council of Elders who helped us work out an agreement we both could live with. He agreed to get a part time job to supplement our income, and I compromised by agreeing to set the thermostat higher in the evening when he was watching television. As an added benefit to this amicable resolution, Grizzly came to enjoy his work in the mornings of delivering hot meals to the elderly, making many friends in the process.

Generally, these meetings work out well with both parties going away satisfied. However, there may occur times when neither party will be happy with the resolution. In such cases, it is wise to keep them at the table until everyone understands each other's needs more fully, and an amicable decision has been reached. If they refuse to work out their problems, it may be necessary for you to intervene by placing a restriction on them that neither will appreciate. Though this may seem punitive, it actually will help them overcome their stubborn pride and come to an agreement in a shorter period of time, while restoring order and harmony to the whole.

The Use of Disciplinary Action

At times you will come across a situation with an Alter who warrants immediate disciplinary action. This could include any misconduct from stealing, to, wittingly, physically endangering the body you all must share. In such cases, it is imperative that you immediately enforce the "ground rule" laws you all agreed upon in your "Bill of Rights", such as "each Alter must take responsibility for his or her own actions and issues". Enforce appropriate restitution promptly, so as to ensure everyone's safety and to discourage other Alters from inappropriately "acting out".

However, as the saying goes, "The punishment should never exceed the crime." This only promotes further rebellion and bad feelings. Be fair, honest, and caring when you administer consequences making sure they understand where they were in error. Respect how the person might feel, even encourage them to suggest a disciplinary action for themselves, and anticipate any problems that may arise with this person. For example, Erick (aka The Big Cutter), suggested his own consequences after endangering our body when he was on a drinking binge. He decided, since it was a chore he hated, that he should do dishes for a week as restitution for his thoughtless, inconsiderate behavior. We felt good that we didn't have to get into an argument with him, and he felt better about himself by making amends on his own.

It is always preferable if you can establish calm communication with the offender and enlist their cooperation. However, at times like this, an Alter may have an old tape loop running in his head that is aggravating him, resulting in an unproductive attitude. Be kind in conveying your understanding of his feelings, but try to make him see the error of his ways and how it has affected others.

In the event the Alter becomes abusive, do not attempt to control the situation alone. Call upon Alters you know can handle the offender physically, should that become necessary, and try to quell the situation again with their presence. Most times, the offending person will settle down and take his consequences. If he is able to accept the "fallout" of his undesirable actions, praise him for taking responsibility for himself and show him through your increased respect of his character. This, he will remember the next time, and will be less likely to cause a scene.

Should you encounter a dangerous Alter while in dysfunction or psychosis, flagrantly disregarding the rights of others, or refusing to take responsibility for his or her actions or make amends, it would be wise to consult with a professional about a specific course of action for safe keeping, as well as to establish a "lifeline" should an emergency arise. However, if you must battle this out alone, we suggest the creation of a "blow-out" room within your system that can lock in an Alter, sort of like an observation or quiet room in a hospital. It would be beneficial to place in it a punching bag and safe objects that an enraged person could release his aggressions upon. This will also drain him of his hostility quicker, so he can calm down and become more rational.

When he is no longer feeling the need to hurt someone, you might approach some communication with him. If he is receptive, ask him, or her, what was happening that triggered such behavior. If they remain non-communicative, you might softly express what it is like to be on the other end of their wrath. You can further explain, that though it was once necessary to endure unjust abuse, and you certainly had your share (signaling to them they were not the only ones), that time has passed, and inroads have been made in healing and creating a loving environment that you would like them to be part of, when they are ready. Further, as a community, it was decided towards that goal, that violence can no longer be tolerated as it once was. The choice is his. He can either learn to be productive and cooperative with others, or, he will be left alone or frequently find himself locked up for the benefit of the family.

Reiterate that you hope he will choose to be part of the family because you admire his strength and courage. Acknowledge that you recognize his actions are the by-products of the abuse he *unjustly* received, and you wish for his recovery, but, misdirecting his energy and venting his unjust abuse on the others is just like what he received. Two wrongs do not make a right. Though you hope he chooses to get along with everyone, you will respect his decision. If he seems non-aggressive and considerate of what you have said, then quietly open the door, walk away, and allow him to leave.

This is not the kind of treatment he is used to, and it may take some time before he recognizes your caring justice. Be sure to give yourself a large pat on the back for acting compassionate and forgiving to an extremely distressed soul, in a way that was never shown you. Congratulations! In doing so, you have overcome the most destructive aspect of conditioning by abusers. You have broken the cycle of "man's inhumanity to man", which continues from generation to generation, each and every time caretakers callously vent on their children and on subordinates in the workplace.

To act better towards others than those who have abused you, is a wonderful credit to your character, and the best possible teacher to abusive Alters who know you have endured the same, but managed to grow beyond them. This shows them there is hope, and there is justice if you work hard to make it that way.

"Can We All Get Along?"

Jamie's in my make-up
Beth took my dress
I can't find my wallet
And my room is a mess.

Someone ate my sandwich
The chaos has been par
I'm late for an appointment
And Frank misplaced the car.

I want cooperation
And respect for me please,
Where's the Inner Self Helper
To protect you when you need?

I rallied a town meeting
Just to tell them what I thought
Three and a half hours later
The culprits were finally caught.

Everyone finally voted
The council all agreed
Scheduling is essential
To accommodate our needs.

Now Beth dresses the body
We all eat the lunch
Frank is our chauffeur
What a well organized bunch!

Chapter Six

Working Through Crises

You Can Expect Crises

Everyone in the world has had to work through a personal tragedy or crisis. It is an inherent part of life. No matter how proficiently you run your family, the fact still remains that we all experience stressors that can become overwhelming and unmanageable. Generally, there is little we can do to prevent crises. However, whatever the perceived catastrophe is, be it crushing financial problems, ill health, the loss of a love relationship, the death of a dear friend, or the surfacing of painful memories, you can work through them successfully and less stressfully if you have a good plan and network of support already in place.

You should give considerable thought to your crisis plan, as it could mean the difference between working a problem out on your own, or having to be admitted to a crisis stabilization unit. Don't wait till "the horse is out of the barn" before you create a workable plan. It is practically impossible to get an organized effort going with your inner persons after chaos ensues, triggering them into dysfunction. As the saying goes, "an ounce of prevention is worth a pound of cure". In fact, since some of our persons can't read or think and remember details when we are in panic, we bought a memory phone and placed important numbers into memory storage with a symbol next to each that can be deciphered by children Alters.

Start by finding out the local crisis intervention hotline number and post it where the other Alters can get to it. Also, post with the hotline number, the phone number for any therapist you may be working with and a list of numbers for relatives or friends, and places they frequent should you need them in an emergency. For someone in crisis, scurrying around to find a number may be more than they can handle and will cause more distress for the person. Enlist the "Inner Self Helper", immediately, to act as a crisis manager to assist Alters in distress, and make sure he or she is thoroughly briefed in advance of the crisis plan. Having an ally at times like these is extremely important in maintaining the safety of all involved. This is especially true if your Alters operate on the "domino theory", whereby, crises begets crises.

Using Contracts in Times of Crises

When a crisis sets in, try to get the distressed person(s) to make some agreements with you for their safety. Don't make the list too difficult or complicated to adhere to. Doing so, will only further aggravate their sense of inadequacy and exaggerate their loss of control. Keep it simple, and clear, such as contracting with them that they will not hurt themselves without first talking with you, or, that they will wait an additional ten minutes after deciding they can't wait any longer. Should this directive fail, consider helping them to redirect that need to cut or hurt the body to an inanimate object that symbolizes their abusers, and attack that with pins, razor, scissors, etc. But, make sure to monitor them. If they are able to wait the ten minutes then try to get them to wait ten minutes more. Feelings of having to cut, hurt, or kill oneself usually cycle, providing periods of down time in between. If you can stall an Alter's actions to one of these "windows" of down time, you will have another chance to reach their rational side. Furthermore, the longer a person is able to resist their impulses, the better their chances of coming through the crisis unscathed and of achieving a sense of lasting self-empowerment.

Include in these contracts, coping mechanisms that have proven successful to the individual in the past, such as relaxation techniques or entering their sanctuary. When the turmoil begins to subside, update the contact as the person begins to gain control, by removing some of the restrictions and precautions. Allow them to exit the safety room or leave the company of their buddy for short periods of time. Doing so, will give the person a feeling that you trust them, and they will notice that they are, on their own, regaining control.

For instance, during the many times that we were in psychiatric hospitals, we experienced the staff's disciplinary action by being locked in a "quiet room" whenever *they* felt it was necessary for our protection, or, as I've heard a nurse or two say many times, to get us out of their hair. Unfortunately, the staff did not work with us to help us regain control, but instead, locked us up for hours until *they* felt comfortable, or remembered to let us out. They would then, simply, open the door and walked away in indifference. Their attitude did nothing to empower us, but rather humiliated and dominated our process. By helping the person to recompensate and gradually lifting the restrictions, such as asking the person if *they* think it is safe to open the door, is liberating their self-control. If they say yes, lift the restriction of the locked door but ask them to stay inside until *they* feel ready to come back, and for them to talk to someone or process their experience someplace alone peacefully. You will see, the more choice you give to someone, the less resistive they will be and the less likely they are to further act out.

Making Use of the Buddy System

In addition to the previous suggestions, we have found the "buddy system" to be extremely effective in de-escalating crisis situations. The presence of another person, whom one trusts, often serves as an adequate distraction from the distress they are feeling. Now, we are not saying it isn't okay to feel your feelings, because it is. As a matter of fact, it is encouraged, as that is how we work through our pasts. But, in times of overwhelming trauma or pain, we sometimes "can't see the forest for the trees" in determining what is right for us at that moment. I have noticed that it is at these times that impulsive acts of cutting, or hasty suicide attempts take place. Having a trusted friend in close proximity makes self-destructive behavior less likely to occur, and adds a voice of reason to remind them of other options, as well as the progress they have made.

So, in the event of a crisis, the first thing to do is alert everyone to the Alter's state of mind and to take precautions in guarding the body. The person in crisis may not outwardly appreciate your presence, but if it is apparent that leaving this person alone will further perpetuate serious "acting out" behavior, you are obligated to keep them and the body safe, independent of how they may feel about it. Grizzly was such a buddy to Michael when he was having manic psychoses. Michael's inner "Screamers" were driving him to cut himself and the body. He was unable to listen to reason or accept that we were trying to help him. Instead, his paranoia fueled his suspicions that we were out to get him. Grizzly volunteered to protect everyone by shadowing him until his psychosis passed, which wasn't an easy task. For days, we had to tolerate Michael's constant screams to leave him alone, as well as Grizzly's exclamations of exasperation, "God damn it Michael! You get back here!" as he chased him around "Sleepy Hollow" (our inner community). Much to Grizzly's horror, his assignment included sleeping in the same space as Michael, which bothered his sense of manhood. However, thanks to Grizzly's commitment to keep Michael and the rest of us safe, Michael was able to recompensate without harming himself or the body, and even thanked his "buddy" for helping him.

Needless to say, you will have to think and act as a professional would in a similar situation. Place the Alter in crisis on fifteen minute observations, and direct the "Inner Self Helper" or the person's "buddy" to keep track of their activity on the inside, and alert you if the person is trying to gain executive control of the body. Obviously, if the situation has progressed to the point where the Alter is seeking to establish control of the body, it is time for more drastic steps to be taken.

In our system, this means that the person is to be denied entrance to the body at all costs, and at least one guard (or more depending on the tenacity and physical strength of the person in crisis) from the protective branch is placed at the entrance to the body. Under no circumstances, unless to speak with a therapist or counselor, is the person allowed into the body. Even then, the Alter should never be allowed to assume executive control. Have a guard or their buddy share joint space with them.

If the Alter is not amenable to speaking with a counselor, attempt to wear the person down by getting them to take a walk with you, lift weights, meditate, or any other activity the person typically likes. Such activities, if you can get them to participate, are often sufficient to thwart destructive intentions. However, if you find yourself unable to keep up with the energy of the Alter in crisis, and you see that you are losing control over the situation, alert another Alter person to call for help. In our system, we do this by ringing the "meeting bell" we erected just inside our compound. When the bell is rung, certain protective Alters know to respond immediately. Thus, help is only a moment away. You may wish to consider building such an alarm system in your structure.

Building a Time Out Room

Sometimes you will find it impossible to de-escalate an Alter's turmoil, or keep the person from harming themselves despite your crisis intervention efforts. Having constructed a "time out", or "blow out" room inside your system (as we suggested earlier), will come in handy at these times. This does not have to be anything elaborate, so long as it has four walls and a door which can be secured and unlocked from the outside only. In addition, it is wise to pad the walls to provide a safe environment and supply safe objects inside to vent upon.

Two different types of rooms are beneficial for different problems. One is for aggressive, hostile behavior, which includes a heavy punching bag to be used as a catalyst in releasing pain and rage in a non-threatening way. Furthermore, it serves to wear the person down so that self-injurious acts become too much effort to carry out. The other room is for someone seriously depressed with suicidal gestures. This room should have a comfortable cot or pillows, plants, and running water, like a creek, to soothe the pain and sense of hopelessness. You might also consider a few toys for children, flowers, a writing tablet, or loving pets that simply lie there with the grieving person.

As in the example we gave about the hospital staff locking us in and forgetting about us, we encourage you to look after the person incarcerated and work with them to lessen the restrictions as they begin to recompensate. They may wish to talk with someone as they begin to feel better. Avoid being judgmental over actions or problems they have caused to your system and fellow residents. Assure them everyone will have their time of crisis and "crazy making" behaviors, and you hope they will be kind and understanding towards you and the others when it happens to someone else. The kind of tyranny you have all lived under is over, and it is time to *help* those in pain rather than punishing ourselves all the more. Provide them the supportive ear they need, as well as empathy.

Seeking Professional Intervention

When all the above efforts fail to de-escalate the crisis, it may be necessary to enlist the aid of a professional. If you have established a working relationship with a therapist or crisis center ahead of time, it will be easier and less traumatic to get yourself into a treatment facility, or to a therapist's office. Don't let your pride befall you here. Not everyone is able to handle crises on their own. Sometimes it is simply too involved and serious to manage. There is no shame in admitting this, in fact, it shows good judgment on your part. Furthermore, it should be relayed to the distressed person as a chance for them to get themselves together in a safe, therapeutic environment. Present the idea that hospitalization is an opportunity to "get off the world for awhile" without having to concern themselves with the daily pressures of life. Make sure, however, that the therapist understands and agrees, as does the Alter in crisis, that this is not punishment, and that inpatient care will be *short term* (a week or two at the most), just long enough for them to regain control and start to feel better.

Have an arbitrator Alter work with the admitting team, to work out a treatment plan that is acceptable to all. The staff may, initially, be put off by your insistence to be in on treatment decisions, but be direct and concise in your concerns and tactful in expressing your rights. If the hospital's objective is to help you, they will appreciate and recognize your input as an attempt to manage and take responsibility for your own recovery and life.

If they present themselves to know what is in your best interest in a patronizing manner, or that you will be better off leaving the treatment concerns to them, simply make a mental note of it. Then, when the time is right, after you and your Alters have been adequately stabilized, have the arbitrator tactfully address your need for self-empowerment to the administrative nurse or caseworker. Calmly suggest that your therapist thought it a good idea for you to participate with the staff in taking responsibility for your recovery. If they can appreciate how being involved with your management could quicken the process of your recovery, you would like their cooperation. If they insist that you are the patient who must follow their agenda, don't make matters worse by staging a rebellion. You have endured worse. Call your therapist if you have to in order to avoid compounding the crisis. However, work on your release, or transfer, and never go back there again if you can find another facility.

After you are released, you might want to speak with your admitting therapist about the hospital's refusal to treat you as a capable adult, or write a letter to the administrator of the facility to complain about their treatment of you. In doing this, you will be breaking the cycle of dependence and subservience you have probably had for years toward professionals. You will also be making a statement to yourselves that you are worthy individuals who are capable of taking charge and directing your own healing.

O
L
V
CpK

Chapter Seven

Helping Children Alters to Express Themselves

Re-parenting Your Inner Children

It is almost impossible to get children Alters to change their internal scripts of abandonment, betrayal, etc., without investing a lot of yourself in re-parenting them. For those of you who do not understand what re-parenting is, simply put, it is a method for showing the child love, compassion, loyalty, sensitivity to others, and appropriate ways of interacting with one another that abusive parents were incapable, or uncaring in their ability to teach them. Since children learn through imitation, you must express and model for them loving, responsible behavior, and compassion for those in pain.

Overcoming years of negative conditioning imprinted on

fragile, impressionable young souls is time consuming, and requires your best behavior, all of the time. You will have to demonstrate for them that they can trust you to be there for them, to be kind, to care about their needs, and to protect them from all harm, real or imagined. This will not be a simple task, as most children Alters had their spirits broken a very long time ago by cruelly abusive adults who they thought, or were told, they could trust. Furthermore, they have, undoubtedly, experienced countless unfulfilled anticipated or promised rewards in their lifetime, which have set their inner scripts for disappointment when bonding to others. In their eyes, trusting anyone, or anything, means opening themselves up for more rejection, punishment, and disappointment.

You will have to try to understand the child's way of thinking, so that you will know if he or she is preoccupied with a negative agenda, that needs dismantling and reconstructing before any real change can occur. For example, is she running a mental tape loop of years gone by, such as "all adults are dangerous", that will give you some idea where she is stuck? Is she cognizant of the present, or, is she still very much in the past? Similarly, is she afraid to express herself, or, would she cherish the opportunity for human warmth, contact, and understanding?

I found that my children Alters where quite different in their ways of relating to me and the outside world. While one was cute, unaffected, happy to be away from our abusers' home, and very much anchored in the present, another was quite withdrawn and very suspicious of anyone who talked bad about our abuser. They both had totally different realities playing out, and required different methods of re-parenting. For example, Punkies learned that there was no longer a threat of going back to her abusers, and that she would be cared for in the present by nurturing, safe, internal and external support systems. We accomplished this by becoming self-sufficient in the world, and secondly, by modeling for her that we had established inner stability and a network of kind, competent, supportive people inside who would take care of her and resolve disputes amicably. Kelly, however, was very difficult to reach because her limited exposure only saw our abuser giving her gifts for bribes and pleasant play times. She had to learn to respect how everyone else had been devastated by him, and learn to transfer her affections and dependencies to those inside. Through co-consciousness, she heard our truths and had to listen to our horror stories without denying the validity of our torment. Further, over time, our inner persons' kindness toward her replaced the memories she had of the treats, and she realized that our abuser's kindness had only been for self-gain.

It was also necessary to teach each one what was expected of them as a child and participating family member. For instance, they needed to learn that there were times when it was inappropriate for them to be in the body, such as when driving the car, or on the job requiring attention to details, or an assigned task that had to be maintained. When that was accomplished, and they understood it, I was surprised how smoothly my system ran. The wars over time in the body and demands for toys and goodies lessened considerably. In fact, they appreciated the loving attention, reasonable boundaries, and nurturing they received from our family within.

Using Appropriate Touching and Hugging

It is said that children come into this world with every ounce of their attention directed on themselves. Getting their gratification needs met is their primary objective. However, in cases of extreme trauma and abuse, the child soon realizes that his needs are not considered or are a source of aggravation to his parents. What's more, expressing them through crying, pouting, etc. will only bring more scorn and punishment upon themselves. As a result, he or she learns to withdraw, mistrust, and isolate themselves. Eventually, they stop searching for the warm arms of a parent to hold and nurture them and replace that need with fear of contact. Further, a soft or friendly voice may equate in their minds, with the sweet tone "Daddy" or "Mommy" displayed prior to sexually abusing them.

Over time, they give up hoping to find solace and comfort from their traumas anywhere in life, and pine quietly for love and affection in a make believe world they feel will never come true for them. However, as you make inroads with your inner survivors, they will begin to let down their guard. It may take a very long time, but, eventually, they will seek you out and want to spend time with you. Always ask first, but by incorporating hugging and respectful, non-threatening touching, which is how children and infants communicate (not through words), you will touch their pain in places that words cannot. Your affection and unconditional acceptance will help to establish a belief within them that not everyone is out to get them, and that their needs can be met without subjecting themselves to abuse along the way. This is a good time to show them, in word and deed, that you intend to protect them by not letting others, including those within, hurt them anymore.

Appropriate touching and hugging is therapeutically sound in helping a person to desensitize themselves to the effects of severe trauma. It does, however, require consent on the part of the child. To force even love on a child or adult survivor, could cause a "state bound recall" of being out of control of one's fate. This would not be productive in securing the child's cooperation to work within the family's system. Make it a point to ask the child if they wish to be safely touched or hugged. Do not assume that because your intentions are good, that the child will see it that way. Give them control over their bodies and personal boundaries. The more leeway you give them, the more likely they are to responded to your attempts to show them love and understanding. Allow them to be their sweet innocent selves, and you will find yourself looking forward to your time together.

As you establish a rapport with them, experiment to find their individual likes and dislikes. Some, you will notice, will like to have their hair stroked, others will prefer to have their backs rubbed, and still others may just like to sit next to you looking over your shoulder while you read to them. In addition, they may have specific times of the day, or night, when they will be more inclined to seek out your attention. Make mental notes of who likes what, and when, and it will be worth your effort to win their trust.

Setting Aside Plenty of Time for Play

A major concern in winning the trust and admiration of your children Alters, lies in your ability to provide them "time out" for play and fun. Children relate to the world in a very simple way. Setting aside time to indulge their desires may be burdensome to your busy schedule, especially if you work full time, but try to remember that they have been disappointed and abandoned so many times, that your failure to participate as promised could easily throw them back in their progress considerably.

Their wants and needs do not take much imagination to fulfill. A day at the petting zoo, a picnic on the beach, or an hour or two in the park may be all that they require to feel like a respected and appreciated part of your family. They also may wish just to stay home and color in front of the television. Make options available to them and let them decide where and what they would like to do.

If they are unable to make up their mind, which frequently happens, try to avoid getting short with them. They do not understand adult thinking and will perceive your impatience as criticism and disapproval. Be consistent in your attitude and follow through. Do not make promises you know you can't, or won't, keep. Children Alters will experience broken promises negatively, as they simply do not understand logic or appreciate time schedules. They only understand that it has happened before, which equates in their minds with you don't care about them.

Investing in Toys and Stuffed Animals

It is truly amazing how much toys, stuffed animals, and coloring books can change the way a child Alter relates to the needs of the family and the outside world. When we were small, a lot of us were treated cruelly and were not allowed to have, or keep, the things that brought us comfort or that made us happy. This includes pets that were "put to sleep" because our abusers were jealous of the attention we gave them, or sold when money got tight instead of giving up their drinking, as well as dolls that were given away to other little children, particularly cousins, by our abusers.

Now that you are in control of your finances and your possessions, it is time to purchase companions for your inner children. We suggest, however, that though animals are wonderful allies in healing, that you do not adopt a live pet until family stability and cooperation is well established to ensure that the animal's needs will always be considered and attended to. Maybe, if an Alter child really wants a live pet, you could agree to it at a time sometime down the road, if the child demonstrates responsibility and works hard on the family reorganization plan, as well as his or her personal issues.

In the meantime, take the children, and be prepared for a lot of different purchases, to something like Toy's R Us, or Child World, and let *them* pick out their new friends. You will probably drop quite a bit of change there, as each child should be allowed to get the objects they like the most. You might consider doing this piecemeal if your budget is low. Just be sure that each child Alter has his or her day to get a toy, and stick to a schedule they can mark on the calendar, otherwise, they will become very jealous of one another. Encourage their individual differences and avoid making suggestions according to their age and gender. One might absolutely adore a big stuffed Panda bear, while another my choose a doll house with miniature furniture and inhabitants that she can change around to suit her needs. Similarly, a boy Alter may prefer to get a dump truck, or boats for the bathtub, though there is no need to stigmatize the boys and girls. Let them get what will satisfy their "inner child", even if it's a doll for "Johnny" and a truck for "Susie". Do not limit them as to what they may buy if you can possibly help it, the money you spend now will be a worthwhile investment in your overall recovery and emerging stability.

We also suggest that while you are there, you purchase a game or two for the entire family to play such as Checkers or Backgammon. Make sure the skill level is appropriate for many different ages. Scrabble and Life, though they may be fun for the older Alters, will not be easily understood, or appreciated by children. Give the inner family a say in the choice of this new entertainment, and buy miscellaneous toys that everyone can use like Lego building blocks, or a Crayola paint set. Also, invite the older persons within (yourself included) to purchase things that appeal to them and nurture their own "inner child", to rebuild their loss of joy, creativity, and spontaneity.

One final suggestion on the subject of toys and companions, is to purchase objects which are portable and can be taken with you to a therapist's office or group setting. Some therapists already have toys available for child clients to play with, however, your inner people will feel more comfortable, secure, and trusting with their own possessions and friends. You might also consider buying one of those Referee Dolls that came out a few years ago. They're great for releasing anger and frustration, as well as pain. The arms, legs, and head are attached with velcro so you can yank them off when you're upset. These make wonderful gifts for survivors who wish to express their rage toward their abusers through physical means. You, simply, imagine the doll as your abuser and start tearing away as you cathart, scream, and vent your pain.

If you are embarrassed to walk down the street with stuffed animals and children's games tucked under your arm, get a big canvas bag to cart them around. Believe it or not, a good portion of the adults that stare at you, inwardly, envy you and wish they could carry around their stuffed buddies!

Including Children Alters in All Family Matters

Involving children Alters in the day to day running of your family, will help to restore a sense of worth within themselves. Value their input, and never make light of their concerns or worries. They, too, have a lot of past 'garbage' to learn to overcome in matters of family relationships. By including them in the family dynamics, you are inadvertently telling them they are okay, loved, wanted, and needed. This may try your patience considerably in light of all the practical tasks you have to do, but imagine the horror of finding yourselves back in chaos and total dysfunction because a child Alter wants to die.

One of the greatest additions young kids serve in group problem solving sessions, is their unobstructed view of things because their needs are so simple. They don't get lost in complications and inner conflict, and can often see straight into the hearts of other people because they aren't muddled in their own thoughts. In addition, their simplistic ideas sometimes yield just the right solution to a difficult problem you may be grappling with. For example, when we were trying to quit smoking we found it all but impossible because various addicted Alters would randomly, and secretively, "bum" cigarettes off of strangers. Consequently, this kept the body addicted and craving cigarettes. Talking about the "slips" after the fact, didn't keep the persons from going "off the wagon". Then one day Jessie said, "Why don't you have daily support groups, like they do in Alcoholic's Anonymous, to share our distress?" It was a very simple idea, one that had been used successfully by other people for years. It was just the ticket for us as we found talking about our cravings prior to our relapses, diminished our compulsions. However, though we did manage to cut down considerably, we unanimously decided later on that it just wasn't the right time for us to quit.

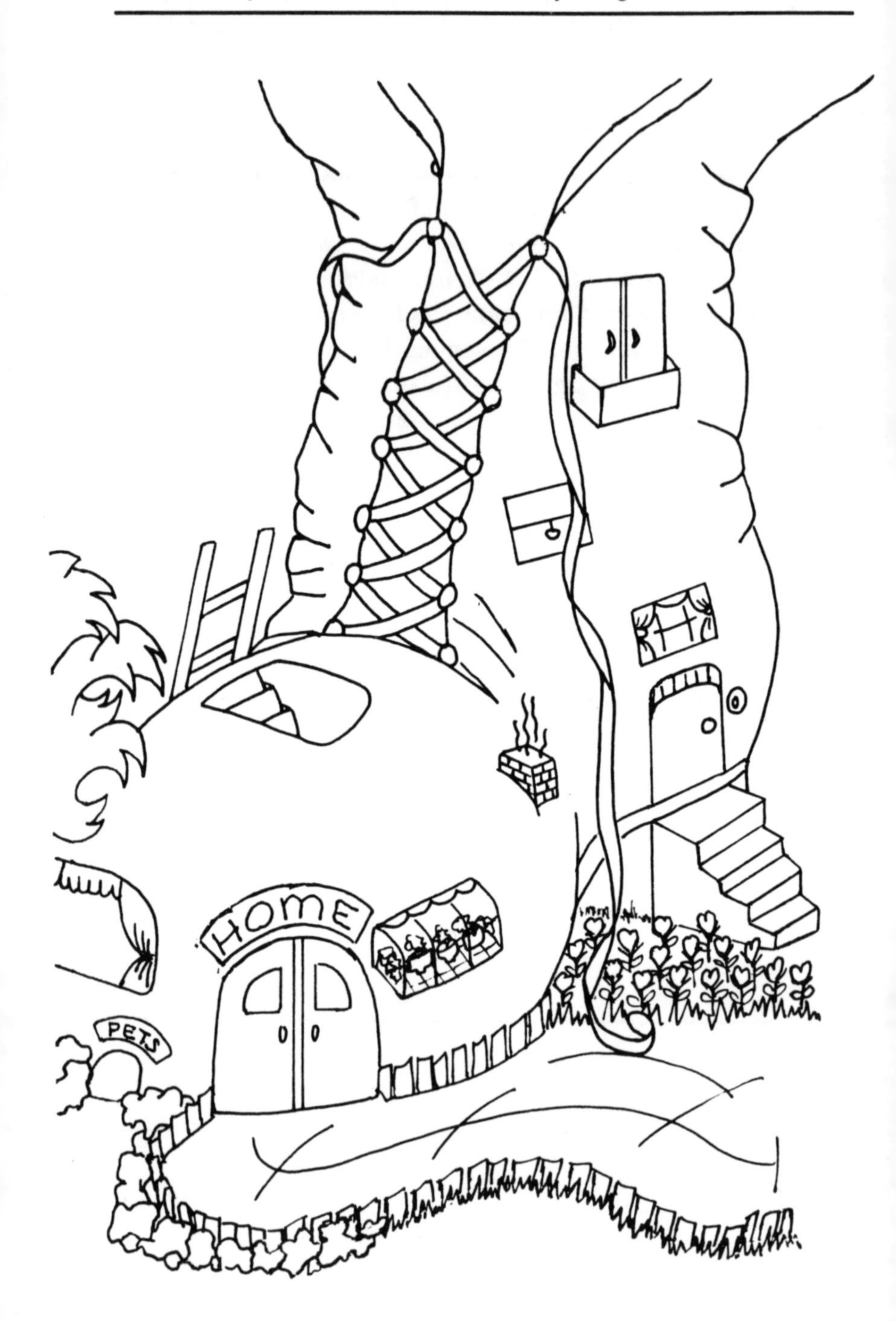
HOME
PETS

Chapter Eight

Living as a Productive, Loving, and Harmonized Family

Maintaining the Health of the Body

We realize we have given you a lot to try out and to think about in the previous chapters of this book. However, if you have stayed with us, and worked the suggestions over time, you are probably witnessing positive changes taking place within your system already. Maybe you are noticing that there isn't as much hostility or separate agendas dictating the way Alter persons relate to each other and the outside world. If this is true, hooray! Your family is starting to gel and work together for the common good.

The more healthy and well-functioning your family becomes, however, the greater the likelihood of Alters wanting to spend more time in the body. Since the body acknowledges the Alters as shifts in energy and physical symptoms, take precautions at maintaining its health. It is extremely easy for each Alter to get lost in their activity and forget the needs of the body. When you multiply that by a dozen or so people expressing themselves daily, the body can tire out and become run down rather quickly. This is compounded when one or more of the inner persons, or the body itself, suffers from any kind of physical illnesses or disabilities. Consequently, it is imperative to establish a program of regulated rest, nutrition, and activity to keep your immune system functioning properly. If an immune dysfunction illness is present, then particular care and health habits may require limitations being placed on Alters and their activities within the body.

Our body is diseased with an illness known as C.F.I.D.S. (Chronic Fatigue and Immune Dysfunction Syndrome). Though the switching of the Alters does not pose that much of a strain on our system anymore, because we maintain co-consciousness, our personal hobbies and habits do.

For instance, because we are tired and drained most of the time, Grizzly has learned he can no longer spend hours bent over the engine compartment of the car repairing it. Michael, on the other hand, suffers from disturbing premonitions, generalized anxiety, and paranoia lending him towards insomnia. He used to stay up for days at a time, checking locks and closet doors fifty to sixty times before he wore himself out in exhaustion. Now, though he's a little harder to get through to than Grizzly, he has learned he must take frequent "time outs" from pacing around or perseverating on his thoughts, to lie down and rest. Sometimes, we still have to drag him away kicking and screaming. Regardless of how much energy we may collectively have, a body can only handle so much. Unfortunately, we only have one physical body in which to express all ourselves, requiring that we share it and respect its limitations.

Another devastating aspect of chronic illness and immune dysfunction, are the resurfacing of issues surrounding chronic pain, depression, and the feelings of helplessness and victimization that a survivor believes will follow them their entire life. Desires to circumvent this "life sentence" frequently expresses itself toward suicidal gestures and ideation. It is very hard to separate in the mind and emotions that chronic pain from physical illness as an adult, is not the same pain from the abuse endured as a child. In all fairness, however, it is likely that the accumulated effect of childhood abuse weakened the body's ability to repair itself, as in all stress related illnesses. Consequently, the possibility that permanent damage was done to the body in some cases, is also a consideration which plays acutely in the soul of a survivor who must continue to bear the brunt of their unjust burdens.

In cases of illness and immune dysfunction due to irreparable damage caused as a result of constant childhood traumas, a strong spiritual alliance has been effective in restoring strength within the soul, which also helps mitigate a lack of health and activity within the body. I have witnessed many times where one has derived a sense of purpose, support, and validation through their connection to God, even when there was no such confirmation in the world around them. Though these individuals serve as an inspiration for other suffers on the same path, they, also, were not without their setbacks and dark moments.

Realize that the search for spiritual strength may take one into unchartered territory, and requires you to be "open" to new ideas and experimental with approaches. In fact, one of our tapes *Healing Meditations and Inner Sanctuary Building for Survivors, Multiples, and Their Alters*, was created to help survivors suffering from physical infirmities to begin healing themselves, mind, body and soul, while increasing their connection to God, a Higher Power, or higher self in this process.

Whatever your path in healing and recovery becomes, I must prepare you for something. One of the disillusioning truths I have appreciated in the testimonies of recovering survivors, is that health and well-being is not a constant once you reach a certain point in healing. Periods of poor health and emotional depressions will inevitably follow good ones (as is true for any population), however, the climb toward health is upwardly progressive and the setbacks are more readily overcome.

As is true for the majority of survivors, you and your Alters will have to decide the best health plan for you. This may include daily naps, a regular exercise schedule, and a nutritional regime that all your persons will have to abide by, regardless of who is in the body. This should not be a big problem as some Alters are naturally inclined to exercise or sleep, etc. However, make it clear to them, that their cooperation in regulating their activities will greatly reduce the stress the body experiences in assimilating all the different energies of your inner persons.

Another alternative for some of the Alters carrying their own illnesses, is to merge or fuse with another Alter who is strong, but, perhaps, limited in their role or responsibility and would like to do more. Combining your strengths and qualities could compensate for individual weaknesses and enable a more fulfilling existence for both, or several, that can work well together. You can agree to do this on a trial basis at first, so no one has to make a decision they fear they will be stuck with.

Whatever your "collective" decides to do in managing your illnesses and caring for the body, explain to them that holding the body in reverence will also help to maintain a healthy emotional balance for its occupants. After all, who can be productive and happy when the body is feeling overwhelmed or in pain? Getting this point across might be better achieved by rewarding with special treats, now and again, for younger or less functional Alters.

We suggest that Alters work out a schedule for sharing time in the body so their individual interests are jointly expressed, while the needs of the family are not compromised.

Cultivating Love, Trust, Respect, and Understanding

As you make progress uniting your persons, continue to work on cultivating positive outlooks and feelings among yourselves. Love was something that was lacking or missing completely in our growing up years. The same can be said about respect, trust, and understanding. These are qualities that will need a lifetime of reinforcing. Therefore, it is unfair to expect that such individuals would feel loved and respected, simply, because someone tells them they are. What is required is to show your commitment in all your actions. Others will take note and respond favorably. Like I have said before, you will have to set an example for them, but don't be surprised if they seem baffled or discount your efforts in the beginning.

Do not lose hope if your persons do not respond to you initially, and that your inner environment may take a long time to heal. Change will take time and Alters will respond differently, but it won't happen if you give up. Expect there to be some resistance to change and trust of your positive gestures. They are only acting out of their conditioning. However, after repeated efforts of maintaining positive contact they will "get it" that you are sincere, that you aren't trying to trick them into letting down their guard so you can abuse them, and that you will not abandon them if they care about you.

Of course, respect is a two way street, and the Alters will have to work on learning to love, respect, and trust each other in addition to receiving it. It will be impossible to become well-adjusted if everyone continues in their present ways of thinking and acting out. Consequently, as you receive acceptance and respect, there's an unspoken obligation to show respect and trust in return. It does not have to happen over night, but Alters will expect to see changes toward that end. As the saying goes, "what goes around, comes around."

Pulling It All Together

Now that you have established yourselves as a family, learned all about each other's strengths, weaknesses, fears and hopes, have set individual and group goals, set up a structured health regime, and banned together to change your inner environment, you are well on the road to becoming a "force to be reckoned with". People will relate to you in a different light. By the strength and attitude of determination you have built, achieved by mingling the Alters' talents and reorganizing your efforts, etc., you will encounter very little that is too much for your gang to handle in a productive manner. In addition, you will now be fighting your battles together, instead of individually with little weight, or against each other, as may have been the case in the past.

The more you are able to stand up for yourselves, and each other, the stronger and healthier you will get. You will no longer have to settle for an occasional bone of friendship, people will want to spend time with the loving, multi-talented, and capable persons you have become. Subsequently, you may find that "singletons" (persons with one mind) envy your diversity and wealth of inner resources.

Furthermore, they will respect you for your determination and hard work at unifying yourselves. They will watch in abject amazement as you establish, and bring to fruition, personal goals no one ever thought you had it in you to accomplish. Their approval, though not necessary for your continued success, will feel good to you and your Alters as an indication that you have turned your inner scripts of failure into ones of success. In addition, people will not be able to flimflam, abuse, or intimidate you as easily as they did before. You will grow to expect the same courtesy and respect from outsiders as you have learned to receive from each other on the inside.

There is, literally, no limit to your growth, or what you can overcome together. For example, when we united and worked out our stuff, The Big Cutter stopped his drinking, cutting, and terrorizing. Michael's anxiety and panic attacks diminished considerably, and Jessie was able to spend more time in reality and less time psychotic. Others, who were emotionally starved for love and attention, worked out healthy intimate relationships with other inner persons and coupled off. In addition, we started a newsletter designed for Multiples choosing not to integrate, lost fifty pounds, rehabilitated ourselves after major abdominal surgery, and later a broken back, and, finally, confronted our abuser. Furthermore, we haven't cut ourselves, had to be hospitalized, or take psychiatric medication for four years now. So, as you can see, the benefits have been numerous and lasting, allowing us the confidence to write this book.

We no longer face life with the attitude that life owes us something in compensation for what happened to us, that we are "damaged goods" no one will ever want, that we are not worthy of goodness in our lives, or that life will never be worth living. Instead, we decided as a family, to use our success in dedicating our lives to helping other Multiples and sexual abuse survivors to resolve their pasts, find peace, and realize their potential. Nothing would make us happier than for our success to become part of your success. We hope we have given you some of the answers you need to achieve that.

Subsequently, the medical profession has looked at us in a different light as well. We have been elevated from the status of a chronically mentally ill patient, to that of a knowledgeable, respected colleague. Hopefully, as you maintain increasing stability, set and realize goals for your own recovery, stand up for what you believe to be right for yourselves, and refuse to let others rule your direction, this will happen for you as well.

Singular minded professionals and the general public are not in a position to ascribe healthy models for someone with multiplicity. Unless they can understand and relate to our inner realities as real, autonomous people who function as whole, complete, fixed individuals within an environmental inner structure, they have no reference points to judge our stability or health. Traditional mental health education only teaches about "normal" (i.e., usual and customary) developmental models with singular awareness, as well as categories of abnormal development with singular awareness. Their general treatment plans attempt to skew the dysfunctional population to conform to integrative "normal" functioning. Unless a particular professional has had personal tutelage and "hands on" experience working with multiplicity in a creative health care system, most of them will attempt treatment models that follow standardized versions of "normalcy" (i.e, singular awareness through integration), simply because they don't know what else to do.

In truth, you have a choice in your treatment goals, and you can change them if it suits your needs. You can organize all your Alters without any integration, as we have, called harmonization, have partial integration that benefits a merger of only some of the Alters, or a large merger resulting in a small collective of functioning Alters called an administration, or total fusion resulting in one person with a single conscious awareness. However, whether you ever achieve and maintain singular awareness after total fusion is uncertain. Whatever your realities and needs are, you, and your family, can be productive within them.

Afterword

In closing, I'd like to leave you with a few words of wisdom we have come to live by that I think might benefit you on your journey. "A house divided among itself can not stand," but a family, firmly united, is unstoppable in what it can achieve. Good luck in your process!

If you have additional questions or comments, or need clarification on any of the material presented in this book, we encourage you to contact us by writing to Artistic Endeavors Publishing, P.O. Box 10224-P, Marina Del Rey, CA 90292 USA. Please be sure to include with your letter, a self-addressed stamped (52 cents) envelope for reply.

Appendix

Resources

The following resources are a small sampling from The Healing Hands Resource Directory, a comprehensive comb bound resource manual of newsletters, services, treatment facilities, Satanic/Ritual abuse resources, organizations, etc., published by Artistic Endeavors Publishing, which can be purchased directly from them by using the order form on page 126.

Multiple Personality Newsletters

M.U.L.T.I.P.L.E.
(Minds Uniquely Linked Together In a Productive Loving Existence)
P.O. Box 10224-P
Marina del Rey, CA 90292 USA
(Bimonthly international newsletter and educational forum emphasizing choice for people with MPD/DD, and treating professionals, but is especially designed for those newly diagnosed and those choosing not to integrate. Subscription order form on page 125.)

B.E.A.M.
(Being Energetic About Multiplicity)
P.O. Box 20428
Louisville, KY 40250-0428
(An expressive newsletter for people with MPD)

The MAZE
P.O. Box 7917
Bonney Lake, WA 98390-0988
(Bimonthly international newsletter specifically for people who have MPD or one of the other dissociative disorders)

MPD Personalities
1163 East Ogden Ave., #705-136
Naperville, IL 60563-1600
(Bimonthly newsletter for people with MPD and their personalities)

Multiple Perspectives
101-9181 Main Street
Chilliwick, B.C. V2P 4M9
Canada
(Newsletter for survivors with MPD)

Justus
P.O. Box 1121
Parker, CO 80134
(Newsletter intended to provide information and opinions related to MPD and ritual abuse issues)

Multiple Care Unit
P.O. Box 82,
NDG
Montreal, Quebec,H4A 3PA, CANADA
(Humor newsletter about MPD for those currently, considering, or not in therapy)

Pro-Survivor Newsletters

S.H.A.R.E.
(Support Help And Resource Exchange)
P.O. Box 7917
Bonney Lake, WA 98390-0988
(Bimonthly international newsletter for partners, friends, and family members living with people who have MPD/DD.)

Stand Fast
P.O. Box 9107
Warwick, RI 02889
(Newsletter for partners and friends of MPD and incest survivors)

Support Groups, Workshop Presenters, and Resource Agencies

M.U.L.T.I.P.L.E.™
P.O. Box 10224-P
Marina Del Rey, CA 90292
(310) 578-1371
(Facilitated & peer run M.P. support groups. Educational workshops and inservice trainings)

Monarch Resources
P.O. Box 1293
Torrance, CA 90505-0293
(310) 373-1958

PARTSSS
(People And Relatives Together Supporting Special Survivors)
223 Auburn Way North, Suite 123
Auburn, WA 98002
(Support/growth options for MPD's and loved one)

PRISM/PROUD-D
P.O. Box 263
Barstow, CA 92311
(619) 577-6397
(Support groups for MPD, and supporters of Multiples)

The Sidran Foundation
2328 W. Joppa Road, Suite 15
Lutherville, MD 21093
(410) 825-8888

International Society for the Study of M.P. & Dissociation
5700 Old Orchard Road, First
Skokie, IL 60077-0124

Real Active Survivor
P.O. Box 1894
Canyon Country, CA 91386-0894
(805) 252-6437
(M.P. workshops designed to assist the therapist and client in addressing many M.P. challenges)

Audio/Video Tapes

Artistic Endeavors Publishing
P.O. Box 10224-P
Marina Del Rey, CA 90292
(310) 578-1371
(Three tape series on self-directed healing for general survivors, Multiples and their Alters. Order form on page 127.)

Cavalcade Productions
7360 Potter Valley Road
Ukiah, CA 95482
(Professional video tapes on MPD and Satanic/Ritual abuse)

Truth Telling Tunes
Ginny Frazier
P.O. Box 23272
Cincinnati, OH 45223
(Performs her "Songs of Recovery" at concerts, workshops, and classroom programs. Songs available on Tapes and C.D.'s)

Treatment Facilities for Multiple Personality & Dissociation

Center for Dissociative Disorders
P.O. Box 9136
Albany, NY 12209
(518) 462-0213

Columbine Psychiatric Center
8565 S. Popular Way
Littleton, CO 80126
(303) 470-9500

Center for Dissociative Disorders
College Hospital
10802 College Place
Cerritos, CA 90701

Abuse and Dissociative Disorders Recovery Unit
HCA Dominion Hospital
2960 Sleepy Hollow Road
Falls Church, VA 22044

Sheppard Pratt
6501 N. Charles Street, Box 6815
Baltimore, MD 21285-6815

Sierra Tucson
16500 N. Lago Del Oro Parkway
Tucson, AZ 85737
(800) 624-9001

Shadow Mountain Institute
6262 South Sheridan
Tulsa, OK 74136
(918) 492-8200

Pennsylvania Hospital Dissociative Disorders Program
111 North 49th Street
Philadelphia, PA 19139
(303) 470-9500

Rush North Shore Medical Center Dissociative Disorders Unit
9600 Gross Point Road
Skokie, IL 60076 (708) 933-6685

Charter Hospital of Dallas Dissociative Disorders Unit
6800 Preston Road
Plano, TX 75024
(214) 618-3939

Brattleboro Retreat
Unit Taylor One
75 Linden Street, P.O. Box 803
Brattelboro, VT 05302-0803 (800) 345-5550

The Cloisters
P.O. Box 1616
Pineland, FL 33945 (813) 283-2866

St. Boniface General Hospital Dissociative Disorders Clinic
409 Tache Avenue
Winnipeg, MB CANADA R2H 2A6

Sexual Trauma Program
River Oaks Hospital
1525 River Oaks Road, West
New Orleans, LA 70123

Satanic and Ritual Abuse Newsletters and Services

gum on your paws
5505 Valmont Road, #97
Boulder, CO 80301

Justus Unlimited
P.O. Box 1121
Parker, CO 80134

Survivorship
3181 Mission Street, #139
San Francisco, CA 94110

Ritual Abuse Project
5431 Auburn Blvd., #215
Sacramento, CA 95841

S.O.A.R. (Survivors of Abusive Rituals)
P.O. Box 1776
Cahokia, IL 62206-1776

Reaching Out
1296 E. Gibson Road, #218
Woodland, CA 95776

Incest/Sexual Abuse Survivor Resources

Pastels and Playing Cards
P.O. Box 10224-P
Marina Del Rey, CA 90292
(310) 578-1371
(Newsletter for adult survivors of childhood sexual abuse who have been abused, invalidated, misdiagnosed, over-medicated, or, otherwise, oppressed or re-victimized by the members of the mental health system.)

S.O.F.I.E. (Survivors of Female Incest Emerge)
P.O. Box 2794
Renton, WA 98056-2794
(Newsletter for survivors of childhood sexual abuse perpetrated by females. Pen-pal program for survivors.)

Voices in Action, Inc.
The Chorus
P.O. Box 148309
Chicago, IL 60614
(Survivor newsletter and services.)

VT.I.S.E.E (Vermont Incest Survivors Enlightened and Empowered)
P.O. Box 82
Milton, VT 05468-3525

Survivors of Incest Anonymous
P.O. Box 21817
Baltimore, MD 21222-6817

Incest Survivors Resource Network International (ISRNI)
P.O. Box 7375
Las Cruces, NM 88006-7375

Not Alone Anymore
738 Main Street
Box 171
Waltham, MA 02154
(Survivor newsletter and pen-pal program)

Body Memories: Radical Perspectives on Childhood Abuse
P.O. Box 14941
Berkeley, CA 94701

Incest Resources, Inc.
46 Pleasant Street
Cambridge, MA 02139

The Healing Woman
P.O. Box 3038
Moss Beach, CA 94308

H.E.A.R.T.
K. Sommer & Associates, Publishers
1030-E Summit Road, Suite 189
Elgin, IL 60120

Write To Tell
6257 Longford Drive-2
Citrus Heights, CA 95621
(Newsletter by and for abuse survivors, as well as allies in our healing)

Women's Recovery Network
P.O. Box 141554
Columbus, OH 43214-9879

Mississippi VOICES for Children and Youth
P.O. Box 8212
Jackson, MS 39284

Virginia Child Protection Newsletter (VCPN)
Psychology Department
James Madison University
Harrisonburg, VA 22807

Treating Abuse Today
2722 Eastlake Avenue E., Suite 300
Seattle, WA 98102

Family Violence & Sexual Assault Bulletin
1310 Clinic Drive
Tyler, TX 75701

Surviving Spirit
P.O. Box 547
Concord, NH 03302-0547

Breaking the Silence
P.O. Box 67035
Lincoln, NE 68506-7035

Healing Our MEmories (HOME)
P.O. Box 1604
San Anselmo, CA 94979-1604

To Tell The Truth
P.O. Box 8117
Santa Fe, NM 87504

General Healing and Mental Health Newsletters

Write To Heal
6257 Longford Drive-2
Citrus Heights, CA 95621
(Newsletter by and for people who have survived wounds such as abuse)

Journey
P.O. Box 30006
Seattle, WA 98103

Dendron
Clearinghouse on Human Rights & Psychiatry
P.O. Box 11284
Eugene, OR 97440-3484

National Association of Psychiatric Survivors
P.O. Box 618
Sioux Falls, SD 57101
Changing Image
Connecticut Self Advocates for Mental Health
1732 Ellington Road
So. Windsor, CT 06074

Mouth
61 Brighton Street
Rochester, NY 14607

Self-Inflicted Violence Newsletters and services

The Cutting Edge
P.O. Box 20819
Cleveland, OH 44120

Clergy Abuse Newsletters and Networks

SNAP News
8025 Honore
Chicago, IL 60620

Linkup
P.O. Box 1268
Wheeling, IL 60090

Survivor Connections
52 Lyndon Road
Cranston, RI 02905-1121

I.C.K. & Others
520 Washington Blvd., Suite 534
Marina Del Rey, CA 90292
(310) 822-1895

Suggested Reading List

PLEASE NOTE: The inclusion of resources in this book does not constitute a recommendation. Some treatment facilities, agencies, etc., that purport themselves as treatment and healing centers for MP&D, have been reported as non-believers of the MPD diagnosis. Please, *always* check out every resource (from any source) thoroughly before enlisting their services.

* If you would like additional resources, you may purchase *The Healing Hands Resource Directory* by using the Order form on page 126.

The Courage To Heal
by Ellen Bass and Laura Davies

Multiple Personality Disorder: Explained for Kids
by Boat, B & G Peterson, 1991

Multiple Personality Disorder From The Inside Out
Edited by Barry Cohen, Esther Giller & Lynn W.
Sidran Press, 1991.

Multiple Personality Gift: A Workbook for You and Your Inside Family
by Jackie Pia, 1991.

Healing The Incest Wound
by Christine A. Courtois

My Tattered Heart & "My Tattered Heart" too...
by Grace Jewell Fisher
Hearts-A-Glow, 1993.

Ritual Abuse: What It Is, Why It Happens, How to Help
by Margaret Smith
Harper San Francisco, 1993.

Outgrowing The Pain Together
by E. Gill, 1992.

Living With Yourselves: A Survivor Manual for People with Multiple Personality
by Sandra Hocking, Launch Press, 1992.

Secret Survivors
by E. Sue Blume

Returning To Herself
by L.J. StarDancer

Women's Sexuality After Childhood Incest
by Elaine Westerlund, 1992.

Satan's Children: Shocking True Accounts of Satanism, Abuse, and Multiple Personality
by Robert S. Mayer, Avon Books.

United We Stand: A Book for People with Multiple Personalities
by Eliana Gil

Ritual Child Abuse: Discovery, Diagnosis, and Treatment
by Pamela Hudson
R&E Publishers, 1991.

Allies In Healing
by Laura Davis.

Voices
by Trula M. LaCalle, Ph.D.

Out of Darkness
by David Sakheim and Susan Devine
Lexington Books.

The Multiple's Guide To Harmonized Family Living: A Healthy Alternative (or Prelude) To Integration
by Tammy Colleen Whitman & Susan C. Shore, Ph.D.
Artistic Endeavors Publishing, 1994.

When the Other Woman Is His Mother
by Faith Brodie

When Rabbit Howls
by The Troops of Trudi Chase

Recovering from Sexual Abuse & Incest: A Twelve Step Guide
by Jean Gust & Patricia Sweeting
Mills & Sanders, 1992.

Index

Information Request Form

for Workshop and MPD Crisis Management Consulting Services

Please send me information on the following services:

☐ M.U.L.T.I.P.L.E.'s workshops for professionals and survivors on M.P. crisis management and stabilization.

☐ Fee information and pertinent details on M.U.L.T.I.P.L.E.'s "hands-on" MPD crisis management and stabilization telephone consulting service for professionals treating Multiple Personality clients.

I am a: (please check which applies)

____Survivor ____Therapist ____Pro-survivor

Name:____

Agency____

Address:____

City/State/Zip____________________________________

Phone No. (______) ____________________ ext.__________

Send to:

M.U.L.T.I.P.L.E.™
Crisis Management Services
P.O. Box 10224-P
Marina Del Rey, CA 90292 USA

(Please enclose a #10 self-addressed 52¢stamped envelope for reply.)

Subscription Order Form

for M.U.L.T.I.P.L.E.™ Newsletter

Please start my subscription to M.U.L.T.I.P.L.E., a bimonthly, international publication emphasizing choice for people with MPD/DD, and treating therapists, but especially designed for M.P.'s newly diagnosed and those choosing harmonized family living as a way of life.

Cost:
$30.00 a year (6 bimonthly issues) in the United States.
$36.00 a year (U.S. currency) for all other countries.
(Includes shipping in plain envelope .)

Sales Tax:
All CA residents must add 8.25% sales tax.

_____Personal check ___Money order. Enclosed $__________

Name:____

Address:____

City/State/Zip____

Telephone: (____)______________________________________

Send to: Artistic Endeavors Publishing
P.O. Box 10224-P
Marina Del Rey, CA 90292 USA

(Sample issues are available for $5.00 U.S. $6.00 all other countries)

Directory Order Form

for

The Healing Hands Resource Directory

This easy access book contains 1,600 national and international listings of sexual abuse, clergy abuse, and Satanic/ritual abuse survivor newsletters, Multiple Personality and Dissociative Disorder treatment facilities, easy access listings of mental health agencies, psychological associations, schools and institutes, therapists, clinics, as well as support groups, audio and video services, miscellaneous services, and a literature list for M.P.D., sexual abuse survivors, and treating professionals.

Cost:
Non-professional survivors: $20.00 + $3.00 S&H in the U.S.
Therapists, Organizations, etc.: $40.00 + $3.00 S&H.
Foreign orders : Add $2.00 extra for S&H. (U.S. currency only).

Sales Tax:
California residents must add 8.25% sales tax.

_____Personal check _____Money order Enclosed $_________

Name:____

Address:____

City/State/Zip_____________________________________

Telephone: (_____)_________________________________

Send to: Artistic Endeavors Publishing
P.O. Box 10224-P
Marina Del Rey, CA 90292 USA

(Please allow 2-4 weeks for delivery)

Tape Order Form

for Self-directed Healing Tape Series

Tape 1: *Healing Mediations and Inner Sanctuary Building for Survivors, Multiples and Their Alters.*

Tape 2: *Establishing Co-Consciousness and Cooperation Among Alters During Abreactive Experiences.*

Tape 3: *Breaking Down The Lingering Power of Abusers Through Reframing and Inner Child Work.*

Cost:
Non-professional survivors: $10.00@ + $3.00 S&H for the first tape, $2.50 for each additional tape. $15.00@ for professionals + $3.00 S&H for the first tape, $2.50 for each additional tape. (All other countries sustitute $5.00 S&H (air mail) for the first tape, and $2.50 for each additional tape.)

Sales Tax: California residents must add 8.25% sales tax.

Please send the self-directed healing tape(s) I have indicated in the space below.

____

____

____

____

____Personal check ____ Money order Enclosed $__________

Name:____

Address:____

City____

Send to: Artistic Endeavors Publishing
P.O. Box 10224-P
Marina Del Rey, CA 90292 USA

(Please allow 2-4 weeks for delivery)

Book Order Form

Please send me my own copy of *The Multiple's Guide To Harmonized Family Living: A Healthy Alternative (or Prelude) To Integration.*

Enclosed is my check/money order for $16.95 + $3.00 shipping and handling ($5.00 S&H for air mail to all other countries).

____ Please add my name to your mailing list and send information on upcoming publications and events.

Sales Tax:
California residents must add 8.25% sales tax.

____Personal check ____Money order Enclosed $__________

Name:______________________________________

Address:____________________________________

City/State/Zip_______________________________

Telephone: (______) __________________________

Send to: Artistic Endeavors Publishing
P.O. Box 10224-P
Marina Del Rey, CA 90292 USA

All FOREIGN ORDERS MUST BE IN U.S. FUNDS!

(Please allow 4-6 weeks for delivery)